SHOCK TO THE SYSTEM

A sequel to What Vets Don't Tell You About Vaccines

Catherine O'Driscoll

G000275896

Abbeywood Publishing
Distributed by Canine Health Concern
www.canine-health-concern.org.uk

Distributed by
Canine Health Concern
Box 6943
Forfar
Angus
Scotland
DD8 3WG

Please see our website for current contact details
www.canine-health-concern.org.uk

ABOUT THE AUTHOR

Catherine O'Driscoll founded Canine Health Concern after two of her young dogs died. She asked why, and now shares the answers with dog lovers so that both animals and humans can experience happiness and good health. She currently lives in Scotland with her partner Rob Ellis, and three canine friends – Guinnevere, Edward and Daniel.

Also by Catherine O'Driscoll

The Golden Retriever Companion, a chronicle of joy

Who Killed the Darling Buds of May?

What Vets Don't Tell You About Vaccines

Further Education

Canine Health Concern runs Foundation in Canine Healthcare courses for people who love dogs and who wish to optimise their friends' health. Catherine O'Driscoll also teaches Emotional Freedom Technique to Practitioner Certification level, and Advanced EFT. For information about these courses, or to join CHC

please email Rob Ellis – Rob@Carsegray.co.uk, or take a look at our website – www.canine-health-concern.org.uk.

NOTE TO READERS

Before following any of the advice in this book, readers should know that in many countries it is illegal to diagnose or treat any animal except your own unless you are a fully qualified veterinary surgeon, or unless a veterinary surgeon has referred an animal to you for treatment. This book is not intended to substitute any professional veterinary treatment. Indeed, we take great pains to assert that veterinary surgeons are invaluable members of the community, possessing a great wealth of knowledge, and that the support of a skilled vet is mandatory for the health of your animals. We suggest only that you choose your vet with care, and work alongside him or her for the optimum benefit of your animal friends.

To Robert
who seeks neither to control
nor be controlled,
and who practices unconditional love;

and to the animals and people
who have filled my heart with joy

Contents

FOREWORD

As with many dog-lovers, from birth, through family life, into independence, and through to full adulthood and beyond, I always had a dog to enrich my life, and I used my knowledge as far as it was available to me at that time.

In 1989 I had two wonderful German Shepherd Dogs, Samson and Jazar. By 1997, Jazar was suffering from a variety of long-running mild to severe skin problems. Samson had hip-dysplasia, and a collapsing immune system. He was on ever-increasing levels of steroids and on a very quick route towards death, to the point where weekly or fortnightly visits to my conventional vet for treatment and/or tests were the norm.

Through referral to a hydrotherapy pool (to help sustain muscles, and alleviate nerve ending damage and his hip problem) I was told about a few alternative therapies and treatments, and given a copy of a Canine Health Concern newsletter. With only the choice of waiting it out, or trying something that I had never heard of, I consulted my conventional vet, the result being that nothing could be done to help Samson other than what I was already doing, and diet would definitely NOT make any difference. You will not be surprised to hear that rather than live with the prospect of no hope, I went for the 'alternative option'.

Within six months Samson was weaned off the steroids, the illnesses that previously caused such frequent visits to my vet were all but eradicated, and I was able to start work on his physical fitness. The end result was a dog who enjoyed four more years of TOTAL health. The prior illnesses were completely eradicated and I was jogging (yes, a dog with hips problems) with him, with no sign of any problems at all apart from some mild arthritis.

Samson's brother, Jazar, now had wonderful and healthy skin and again enjoyed a wonderful last four years of his life. I should also add that my knowledge of canine healthcare and simply knowing my own dogs also increased to wonderful proportions and led to my later study of canine psychology.

Since that time I had infrequent but regular contact by letter (and occasionally by telephone) with Catherine in support of CHC, its aims and most importantly in support of dogs. In 2003 our contact became one of a debate on the issues surrounding the intelligence of dogs, which became long-standing. The debate was based on honesty and open communication between ourselves and moved into a personal friendship, which culminated in my moving to Scotland to join Catherine, where we both run CHC and live together with our wonderful Golden Retrievers Edward, Dannie and Gwinnie.

This foreword is obviously biased but I have to state (at the very least) to anyone and everyone – that dreams can come true if you stay true to your own belief in yourself and not be influenced by the outside world (outside of yourself). This is not only an emotional statement, it is also a factual one. You could say that this foreword is one of self-indulgence, with me being Catherine's partner – but I am the one who knows Catherine best at close hand, (especially with regard to her feelings and thoughts of the past twelve years or so) and even though I am biased, I am also honest.

The CHC campaign, although initiated out of grief and a need for knowledge, has grown and matured into a unique body of work. One that, if it was in the conventional field of science, would have been applauded and deemed ground-breaking by scientific peers. Because CHC has been 'outside' convention, it is there to be shot at from anyone who cares to do so, and quite rightly so! No-one or nothing should be taken 'as read'. What is sad though, is that Catherine is not afforded the same love and consideration that she affords others.

Speaking one's truth can be seen as contentious, arrogant or rude, even if said with inoffensive intent. However, politeness for the sake of politeness can lead to harm and result in untruth.

What you will *not* get in this book, is unsubstantiated fact. What you *will* get is information that is based on science – it is written (and this may surprise a few of you) to give you the opportunity to see for yourselves. It is about more than vaccines, it is about all areas that affect our dogs/cats/horses, and even our own health.

There is also an element of spiritual health and emotional wellbeing covered by this book – and this also relies upon scientific research. If you have read the research (as I have), you will know just how fascinatingly relevant it is also, however surprising that may appear to some.

One of the reasons this book is necessary is that we have all been struggling under a system that does not allow us to see the science for ourselves, and we are constantly being told what to do and how to do it by individuals and establishments.

So, *Shock to The System*? What system? Well, the obvious is, that vaccines represent a shock to the body system. Similarly, other elements such as food, stress, drugs, etc., can provide hefty shocks to the physical body and energy systems. What other systems are there? Well, there are the 'industrial and establishment' systems, and within and around each system, there is the belief system – including the belief system of each and every reader of this book. Catherine gives us food for thought.

Your role is to digest and then decide for yourself.

Rob Ellis Dip ACP (NOCN)

Introduction
A Question of Belief

Readers of *What Vets Don't Tell You About Vaccines* may be surprised to learn in this book that I have gone through something of a change in my way of thinking. Whilst looking for the causes of health and ill health in our dogs over the last twelve or so years, it has become clear to me that the answers are not simply to be found in the physical realm. It's not just about the food we eat, the pharmaceuticals we are prescribed, the environment we inhabit. I can no longer blame vaccines for 'killing' my dogs. I can say that they were instrumental, but they were not the only cause. There is something much deeper that determines health and ill health, life and death.

We see the world not as it is, but as we are. We base our actions, thoughts and behaviours on our values: the issues at the core of life which we consider to be important. We do the best we can with the knowledge we have available. We make friends with others who share our values – our beliefs - and we give our attention to activities which mirror our values. Sometimes, as we go along, we acquire more information, more wisdom, and our beliefs and values can change. I would never have started the Canine Health Concern campaign if I didn't believe that humans evolve and grow, and that we *all* wish, ultimately, to make a positive difference to the life on this planet. What would be the point of campaigning if you didn't think there's a chance of positive change, or you didn't believe in your fellow human beings?

Now we see through a glass darkly, straining through the mist to understand. Progress is made when the mists begin to clear. The process of mist clearing, of reaching understanding, is what interests me these days – because this is what keeps us alive, and keeps us expanding and evolving.

When we love someone or something, we give it our attention. We want to look at the beloved; we can't get enough of them. Conversely, when we dislike or fear something, we look away. We eventually become experts in the objects of our love. None of us can know everything there is to know about everything, and so we specialise. We acquire information in areas that attract us, whether it be in a formal educational setting, or in the school of life.

I became interested in canine health, as a specialisation, after two of my young dogs died, then a third, and after my other dogs began to suffer from debilitating illnesses. I wanted to heal my pain, which necessitated knowing why, and then I wanted to ensure that the other dogs I shared my life with wouldn't suffer the same fate. Meeting others whose dogs had also suffered and died, I was compelled to share what I had learnt, simply because I could not bear the thought of anyone standing over the corpses of their friends asking, as I had done, 'Why did nobody tell me?'.

The parents who raise us give us our values, for better or worse. I was raised by two highly principled people who believed that it was wrong to stand by and keep your mouth shut while your fellow human beings suffered. Because I love the animals, and see them as people with hearts and souls, I couldn't watch them suffer either. Starting Canine Health Concern to share information about canine healthcare was not a conscious decision on my part – it was the result of my early programming.

When I first asked why my dogs had died far too early in their lives, I had no scientific belief system to prevent me from looking in any direction. I was a science virgin. If the truth be known, most of us – even the scientists – are science virgins. We know so much and yet so little.

What I did have, though, was a career behind me of taking scientific and technical briefings, and first understanding, and then transforming, erudite and exclusive words into a language that everyone could understand. It was my job to help sell the complex products and services that I now question. I was capable enough in that career, as a marketing and public relations consultant, to be amongst the highest paid people in the country, working for many of the world's major corporations. My career also gave me a good training in humility: I learnt that if I got it wrong, and failed to deliver the goods for my clients, then I wouldn't get paid. I am equally aware that if I write or say negative things about products, in the *belief* that they are killing both humans and animals, and I cannot substantiate that belief, then my work is not helpful. Therefore I try to throw belief to the wind, and look at what is.

I have another incentive to get it right: I do what I do because I love the animals, and I don't *believe* that animals are any less than human beings. I believe that it matters enormously when a dog, or cat, or horse or even a mouse or rat is made to suffer at the hands of man. I *believe* that when one of us suffers, then the whole world suffers; that

2

what happens to the animals, also happens to man. But I have to concede that the vets who advocate annual shots and processed food for animals might also be animal lovers. I don't believe I have the monopoly on love.

I believe that my dogs died prematurely because of the false beliefs we have about animal husbandry and healthcare, and I believe that animal guardians need, and want, to be better informed so that they can make better choices for their friends. The aim of this book is to be helpful. It asks the question, again, whether vaccines are inherently harmful, and it seeks to expand upon the understanding of healthcare that will mitigate the need for vaccines.

I believe that veterinarians are, in many ways, being misled by the system that educates them, and misguided by the wealthy corporations that shape both educational and political agendas. There is so much knowledge available to the veterinary profession that they are not being given access to through their education, simply because that information does not fit the beliefs of the system that educates them. I seek to be helpful to vets because we animal guardians have a great deal to thank them for. Contrary to popular belief, I do not hate vets – I love vets.

I understand that many veterinarians and scientists believe that vaccines are necessary; that they have halted epidemics. This is the simple part. What I don't understand is that there seems to be so much scientific data to say that vaccines come with serious risks, and yet we are vaccinating far more frequently than we need to. We are being advised by many to vaccinate dogs and cats every year, and horses every six months, even when scientific data shows that this is not necessary, and that vaccination is potentially harmful.

What nobody understands, and nobody seems to know, is how great the vaccination risk is. Will *my* dog die if I give him a vaccine? Will *my* child have brain damage if I give her a vaccine? Will *my* horse produce deformed foals if I give her this vaccine? Is there a way we can remove those at risk from the vaccine programme, and how do we determine who is at risk?

You know, when there is an epidemic, not everyone contracts the disease – even non-vaccinated individuals can withstand viral challenge. Why? Is there anything we can do to boost our loved-ones' immune systems so that they can defeat death without also risking death?

Since Oliver died in 1991, and I discovered alternative healthcare for myself and my dogs, I've been asking myself why the healthcare industry is so divided. On the one hand we animal guardians have highly qualified holistic practitioners telling us that their therapies are safer and more effective than conventional drugs. On the other hand, we are told that the pharmaceutical model is the only properly verified system of healthcare. I've been asking myself why this battle is waging. And, always, at the root of my question, is how can I best care for my animals and myself? Whose belief should I follow?

I've seen alternative therapies work very powerfully in both myself and my dogs over the years, yet many conventional scientists tell us that they don't work, or that there is no evidence to say that they do. A National Health Service hospital consultant, Andrew Lawson, appeared in the *Sunday Times* recently to point out the downside of 'going natural'. He spoke of a rise in mumps affecting the testicles due to the risks people associate with vaccines. He bemoaned the fact that taxpayers money was being used to fund a guide to alternative health. He said that anything that does not harm a patient while helping them must be good – 'but scepticism is not based on a desire to be seen to be 'right', but rather on concerns about mechanisms, safety and efficacy'.

He added, 'you cannot really progress in science unless you accept your theories might be wrong. . . . Orthodox doctors are often accused of not having the right attitude towards complimentary medicine. Well, belief is a poor substitute for knowledge. Healthcare must involve wanting to find the truth or get as near as we can come to it. There is a moral obligation to do this, not least in terms of resource allocation but also so that vulnerable individuals such as cancer patients are not given false hope or, worse, have proper treatments delayed.'

The irony, it seems to me, is that the arguments postulated by this doctor against alternative treatments are the very same arguments I would use to explain why orthodox medicine appears to be failing us and our animals – and why people are looking for alternatives in the first place. The modern medical model doesn't have all the answers, and there is a great deal that is unknown. It seems to me that, if you care about healthcare at all (which, as a patient or client of veterinary services, seems to occur after a terrible tragedy has occurred), then you either join the red team or the green team, and sit on your chosen side of the fence and take shots at the other side. I for one am tired of firing the shots, and I'm tired of being hit. I long for peace – which, interestingly enough – is the place where I now believe good health can be found.

It seems to me that our *beliefs* make us sick or, if we have no beliefs, if we follow blindly, then we are in danger of having other people's beliefs making us sick. *Belief* is probably at the root of all of the problems we face in this world. Think about it: belief stops us from looking at what is.

When we are chock full of belief, there is no ability to allow anything else in. We are blinded by structures of thought that seem to compel us to make incoming data fit into the existing beliefs we have. It has been a major challenge for me to write this book, because I've had to examine my beliefs and throw some of them out – because they would no longer fit with my expanding knowledge. It's not easy to make your way through opposing sides of a debate and allow your mind to be changed. I think a lot of us are going through this process these days, on both sides of the fence, which makes it all the harder to tell others what they should do.

The conventional scientific belief is that vaccines have halted epidemics, and won the battle against death and disease. But what if this is not actually the case? I am not saying, here, that it isn't the case, but that there is quite a body of evidence to suggest that it isn't. Unless you leave room to at least question your own beliefs, then you can never really have confidence in them. They become a flimsy structure that you fear might collapse at any time, so you either run or use violence of some sort, whether verbal or physical, to defend them. It has been painful to find, through the experience of running CHC, that my defences, on behalf of the animals, have been perceived as attacks. I now know that if I want peace for myself, then there is no Peace Fairy likely to descend upon me and make it happen. I know that to be at peace, I have to come from peace. This means that all of us who choose peace, and health, must look for common ground, areas of concordance.

People today, in places like Iraq and Israel, are strapping bombs onto their bodies and walking into crowded places, and killing themselves and everyone around them – in the *belief* that God is on their side; that they will be rewarded in heaven and enjoy the eternal services of numerous virgins. We in the West think that this is a ludicrous and harmful belief, but the people who strap the bombs onto

5

themselves believe in what they are doing enough to die for their beliefs. The mind is a very faulty compass. We shouldn't place too much reliance on it.

It's at those times when we sit back, stunned, and realise we were wrong that the greatest changes can be made. It's when we just don't have the answers that we go searching. This process can be painful – but pain is transitory, it comes and goes like waves upon the shore. We shouldn't give too much power to pain, or allow it to defeat us. The root of the pain I speak of, in fact, lies in the unknowing. It is released when answers are found – and to get to the answers, we have to ask questions.

Have you ever wondered why Einstein made such huge progress for modern science? When he birthed quantum physics, he had no formal training, no received wisdom, to hinder his view. Sadly, after he was applauded and honoured, Einstein believed the publicity that surrounded him. He could no longer admit data that contradicted his beliefs, and quantum engineering, upon which modern computers are based, left him behind.

It is the ability to question that enabled Gary Smith, who you will read about later, to arrive at his theory of inflammation that currently has the scientific world in a state of excitement. Gary was *learning* in an open university system – he didn't inhabit on a daily basis the classrooms, the belief systems, that would limit his ability to question. He didn't think he knew all the answers – he was open to the answers. It is also why children learn so quickly, and why an adult's ability to learn is impaired.

We can all of us see how political and religious beliefs, national, economic and scientific beliefs, create conflict and antagonism. We can see how we're all trying to convert one-another, to have the other fellow agree with us. Our beliefs separate us and create intolerance, and lead to illogical double standards. And because we believe we are so right, we seek to impose our beliefs on others.

But who are we to make choices for other people? Is not each one of us as fallible as anyone else? Do others not have a right to information that will enable them to make choices on behalf of the animals they love? Should we leave it in the hands of those with advertising budgets, and money to grease the research wheels, and those standing in line hoping for funding, to tell us what is true?

The author John O'Donohue spoke of the legacy of free thought left to him by his father: 'There is a divine call to us all in knowing our own minds. The most important place to go out from is where you're at home in yourself. Nobody can tell you that, and if you don't know that, you're vulnerable to abuse from people's opinions, expectations and control. If you know it, you're on your own path of discovery.'

I think that sometimes we are not helpful to our fellow man when we try to protect him from being led astray; when we try to rescue others from their fate through some method of control. We have to keep talking and exploring; we have to refrain from book burning; we have to listen to each other.

As Hermann Hesse said, 'If my life were not a dangerous painful experiment, if I did not constantly skirt the abyss and feel the void under my feet, my life would have no meaning'.

To be free, to honour the trust that our animals, and our children, place in us, we have to skirt the abyss and allow ourselves to be uncomfortable for a while. We have to look at what is, and allow others to explore and learn, and even make 'contentious' statements that question established beliefs. This is the only way to ensure that we 'first do no harm'.

By opting for the 'safe' constrict of belief, we are potentially imprisoning ourselves in illusion.

It is for this reason that I will never tell anyone whether or not they should vaccinate their animals, or their children, or themselves. I will not tell anyone that there is one absolute right food for their dog. Neither will I sit quietly by while other people try to tell me, or you, that you must vaccinate your pet every year, or that you are not intelligent enough to understand this complex subject, but just do as those in authority tell you. There is too much in the current scientific/medical model that is illogical and open to question, and our lives, and our animals' lives, depend upon *us* having the courage to look – to give our attention to what we are doing in the name of love - rather than looking away.

It is hard, in the state of current knowledge, to know what is right for you or your animals. My aim is to provide information that will empower you to make your own loving choices. You know, if you believe something just because everyone else believes it, then you are not thinking. You are a prisoner, sleepwalking your way into the unknown. In this complex world, someone always pays the price when we go sleepwalking.

I believe the animals have come to us to help us in the process of waking up. All we can do is work with them, not for them, listening all the time. We would do well to listen to each other, too.

One
The Background

It started fairly innocently. After two of my young dogs - Oliver and Prudence - had died, and I asked why, I was sent a scientific paper by another dog lover, written by a vet and researcher called Jean W Dodds. Her paper told me, for the first time, that my tragedies weren't particularly unusual. Thousands, if not millions, of dogs and dog owners around the world had experienced what I had experienced. I wasn't necessarily the worst dog owner in the world, as I had feared, failing to keep my friends in good health – there were many other dogs in the same sorry state.

The experiences of dog owners appear to mirror the experiences of parents, horse owners, cat owners – indeed, of any species that is vaccinated.

Dr Dodds' paper explained that there had been a significant increase in the frequency of blood, autoimmune and allergic diseases in the pet population since the introduction of modified live virus vaccines. At around the same time, because my living dogs were ill and conventional veterinary care wasn't helping them, I had made my way to a homoeopathic vet.

The homoeopath, a man called Christopher Day, spent an hour with me and Chappie on that first visit, primarily asking questions. What did Chappie eat? What sort of personality did he have? What was Chappie's medical history? Chris gave me homoeopathic remedies to take home for Chappie, and he gave him acupuncture there in the surgery. Chaps had ruptured both of his cruciate ligaments, and he cocked his leg for the first time in months when we left Chris Day's premises.

While I was with Christopher Day, I asked a question that I had asked every vet I'd met in the previous two years. I explained what had happened to Oliver, and I asked Chris why, did he think, Ollie might have died. Chris asked when Oliver had been vaccinated, and then he told me that, in his experience in practice, 80 percent of illnesses start within three months of a vaccine event. He suggested that Oliver had had a classic vaccine reaction. I have since corresponded with many other dog owners whose dogs became paralysed in their back legs shortly after they were vaccinated, just like Oliver.

9

But paralysis of the rear end is not the only unwanted consequence of vaccination. According to the paper by Dr Jean Dodds, vaccines were also causing autoimmune diseases and allergic reactions in our dogs. One of these was leukaemia, which had killed Prudence in the most horrific and painful way.

According to Dr Dodds, autoimmune diseases have four main triggers.

Of the more than 40 autoimmune diseases, susceptibility to almost all is strongly influenced by genetic inheritance. However, this genetic predisposition must be triggered by something else. That 'something else', capable of triggering a full-blown, life-threatening, autoimmune disease was according to Dr Dodds, either a virus, a vaccine, sex hormones, or stress.

It's ironic, I find, that the vaccines we use in the run from life-threatening viruses also have the potential to kill. I appreciate that this might come across as a contentious statement – but it is nevertheless a true statement.

Autoimmune disease is any disorder involving inflammation or destruction of tissues by the body's own immune system: the body's biochemicals attack cells in their own body. According to the *Oxford Concise Veterinary Dictionary*, 'such disorders result from the activity of lymphocytes (white blood cells which help individuals develop immunity) primed to act in response to self antigens; antibodies, complement, hypersensitivity reactions, and other immune mechanisms may be directed against self tissues'.

To translate this, autoimmune disease is where the body's own biochemicals are attacking the individual's own body. And, according to Dr Dodds, the vaccines we give to our dogs in the belief that we are protecting them, could in fact be damaging them by causing their own bodies to self-destruct in this way.

At the same time, a dog lover sent me an article by an American who claimed he had developed a version of pet food that, whilst being processed, mimicked natural food and promoted life. The article went to great lengths to explain why, in his opinion, processed pet food could not sustain life. This is why there is a chapter on nutrition in this book: because the fuel we put in our bodies, and our animals' bodies, is crucial in matters of health.

The answer to my question 'why?' – why had Oliver and Prudence died – was starting to attract answers. Remember, Dr Dodds

10

had written that autoimmune disease could be triggered by either a virus, a vaccine, sex hormones, or stress. I vaccinated my dogs every year, fed them the dried pet food my vet advocated, and my life was very stressful. Were my dogs being affected by this stress, and were they ill because I was following my vet's advice on nutrition? I didn't really understand how one could influence sex hormones, another culprit in Dr Dodds' list, but it gradually became clear to me that hormones are vastly dependent upon the nutrients available to an individual, as well as stress factors which deplete the immune response.

My ex husband John Watt and I wondered why vets would promote annual shots – especially *annual* shots - when they were so potentially dangerous, and we also wondered why vets advocated commercial pet food rather than food that had been designed by Nature over millions of years to support the wellbeing of canines. Were we substituting the fast-food equivalent for real food to the cost of our dogs?

My background in marketing, and John's Masters degree in systems analysis and operational research, coupled with his background as a statistician and business consultant to many of the world's top corporations – and our devastation at the loss of our young dogs – led to a fairly natural conclusion. We decided to spearhead research that would look at the causes of health and ill-health in the modern dog. Our business backgrounds also told us that vets and medical doctors are educated in a system that relies upon commerce for funding. By spearheading research by dog lovers for dogs, we felt that it would be free of commercial influence, and the findings would be accurate. We founded an organisation called Canine Health Concern to look into the causes of health and ill health in the modern dog, attracting the support of vets and dog lovers around the world.

One of our first pieces of research was the Canine Health Concern vaccine survey, designed to test Chris Day's experience in practice that, where the start date of an illness is known, 80 percent begin within three months of a vaccine event. The questionnaire was devised with the help of Dr Jean Dodds, Christopher Day and Dr Viera Scheibner. It was mailed to members of Canine Health Concern, and some members circulated the questionnaire to friends and neighbours (since we knew it was important that it was also completed by people who couldn't be accused of a bias against vaccines). We also took

11

advertising space in a prominent dog magazine and printed the questionnaire so that any of its 30,000 readers could take part, irrespective of their bias for or against vaccines. In total, we received completed questionnaires for some 3,800 dogs.

The full findings of this survey were published in my book, *What Vets Don't Tell You About Vaccines*. We found – much to our own surprise – that there was a definite statistical correlation between a vaccine event and the onset of a number of specific illnesses. Overall, we found that 66 percent of all illnesses reported by participants occurred in their dogs within the first three months after vaccination. If a vaccine had no bearing on subsequent illness, you would expect to see roughly 25 per cent occurring within each three month time frame making up a year.

Further analysis showed that 49 percent of all illnesses recorded in the survey started within 30 days of vaccination. The figures appear to be even more dramatic when you look at what happens within seven days of vaccination. A massive 29 percent of dogs in the survey who were ill, first became ill within seven days of their vaccine shots. The following figures relate to the percentage of specific illnesses, experienced by dogs in the survey, starting within three months of a vaccine shot:

Allergies – 69.2%
Arthritis – 37.8%
Ataxia – 91%
Autoimmune disease – 55.8%
Behavioural problems – 64.9%
Cancer – 35.1%
Chorea – 81%
Colitis – 65.9%
Diarrhoea – 78.4%
Dry eye/conjunctivitis – 56.9%
Encephalitis – 78.6%
Epilepsy/fits/convulsions – 73.1%
Heart conditions – 39.2%
Kidney damage – 53.7%
Lameness – 66.7%
Liver damage/failure – 61.5%
Loss of appetite – 83%

12

Nasal discharge – 87%
Nervous, worrying disposition – 54.8%
Pancreas problems – 54.2%
Paralysis of rear end – 69.2%
Short attention span – 73.1%
Skin problems – 61.2%
Tumour or growth at vaccine site – 81.1%
Vomiting – 79.7%
Weight loss – 63.1%

Dogs in the survey also – to our extreme surprise - contracted illnesses within three months of being vaccinated against them, showing that vaccines are no guarantee of protection:

Hepatitis – 75%
Parvovirus – 69%
Distemper – 66.7%
Parainfluenza – 55.7%
Leptospirosis – 100%

By chance, I met a television producer and, as we chatted, I told him about the survey and the book I had just published regarding pet vaccination. This chance meeting resulted in Canine Health Concern's work becoming the subject of a prime-time TV documentary in October 1998: World in Action's 'Fatal Attraction'. The programme attracted a huge response and I am told that vets throughout the UK subsequently spent around half an hour per client persuading them that their pet did indeed need their annual vaccine booster. Veterinary receptionists were also inundated with calls from clients cancelling booster appointments.

The CHC telephone helpline was red hot: we had calls from people who had seen the programme after losing their dogs that very same day; the very same day their dogs were also vaccinated. Others wrote in, sending photographs and letters that tore my heart apart.

The veterinary vaccine industry in the UK mounted a PR campaign to refute our findings. The Veterinary Medicines Directorate (which is the government licensing body for veterinary products) asked to study our data. This was what we had hoped for. Indeed, in '*What Vets*' I had called for scrutiny of our research. Unfortunately, the VMD

13

suggested that a consultant paid by Intervet, the UK's leading veterinary vaccine manufacturer, should scrutinise the results. We asked, instead, for an expert who was without bias or commercial interest. The VMD declined.

The government, however, launched a working group to look into canine and feline vaccines. Its interim findings appeared in my letter-box in early 2001. I turned immediately to the page which named the individuals in the working party. There were four people in all. Two were consultants to Intervet, a third was a member of the Veterinary Defence Society Limited, and the fourth was a layperson whose status was not specified. I was dismayed and knew straight away what the findings would be.

Whilst acknowledging that vaccines can cause autoimmune haemolytic anaemia in dogs, and vaccine-site cancer in cats, the working party recommended that we should continue to follow vaccine company recommendations, which meant that we should continue to vaccinate annually.

I wrote eleven letters in all to my MP, who forwarded the letters onto the Minister responsible for Defra (Department for the Environment, Food and Rural Affairs), under whose control the Veterinary Medicines Directorate acts, pointing out that it must surely be wrong that industry consultants sit on government committees to say whether or not their products are used or safe; and that numerous duration of immunity studies showed that annual vaccination was neither necessary nor without harm.

The Minister, Lord Whitty, replied that the paid consultants to the vaccine industry were individuals of the highest repute, so sod off (I paraphrase).

The British veterinary associations also agreed that annual vaccination was a good thing, and continued to advocate annual shots for dogs and cats.

This is despite the fact that, in July 2000, the American Veterinary Medical Association Council on Biologic and Therapeutic Agents (COBTA) had announced:

- When an annual booster vaccination with a modified live virus vaccine is given to a previously vaccinated adult animal, no added protection is provided. Modified live virus vaccines depend on the replication of the virus for a

14

response. Antibodies from previous vaccines do not allow the new virus to replicate. Antibody titres are not boosted significantly, memory cell populations are not expanded. No additional protection is provided.

- There is no scientific data to support label directions for re-administration of MLV vaccines annually.
- Vaccines are not harmless. Unnecessary side effects and adverse events can be minimised by avoiding unnecessary vaccines.

These pronouncements followed the arrival of numerous studies which showed that viral vaccines provide immunity for years, or even life. In addition to this, it had been shown that – to translate the above – modified live virus (MLV) vaccines have no effect if an animal has already developed antibodies to the viruses being vaccinated against. The antibodies simply fight the vaccine, rendering it incapable of doing any further good. Further, vaccines are not harmless.

I just want to emphasise what is being said here, because the above three points are very simple, and very important.

You don't need to vaccinate your dogs, cats, horses, or rabbits against viral disease every year because it provides no benefit whatsoever, and could lead to potential harm.

Despite these facts, the veterinary pharmaceutical industry conducted its own research to refute CHC's vaccine survey findings. It struck back in December 2004, when the following article appeared in Veterinary Times:

POOCH STUDY GOOD NEWS FOR VACCINATED CANINES
Report by Dan Kirk

The second paper of a study conducted by scientists at the Animal Health Trust (AHT) into the correlation between vaccination and ill health in canines is due to be released this month.

Author of the POOCH study, Dr David Edwards told Veterinary Times that the study was conducted in response to the ongoing debate about the safety of vaccination following a Canine Health Concern (CHC) magazine survey back in the 1990s. The CHC survey indicated 10 per cent of dogs became ill within three months after vaccination and was featured in one of the last World in Action programmes in

15

1998.

The paper holds encouraging results for veterinarians and vaccine manufacturers alike.

Long-running debate

Humphrey Grimmett, Schering-Plough's veterinary technical advisor, said the vaccine debate had been raging for almost two decades.

He explained: "The vaccine debate is still ongoing. You've got homeopaths who insist vaccines cause all sorts of immune problems. They want people to believe vets are basically screwing the public by getting them back in for boosters and the manufacturers' are making no effort to change this, which of course is not true."

Dr Edwards indicated that the second paper would show the broader findings of the POOCH study. He outlined how the POOCH questionnaire had been sent out to a random selection of nearly 4,000 clients.

Dr Edwards said: "The questionnaires were designed so that the study hypothesis did not obviously relate to vaccination. A covering letter explained it was a dog health survey seeking to determine how various factors influence dog health.

"As well as questions regarding the dog's household and location, the health status of the dog for a two-week period prior to completion, we asked about vaccination, worming and flea treatments." said Dr Edwards.

"The selection criteria were for dogs that had been seen by a vet within the previous 12 months, or if a transaction had occurred in the dog's name, even if they had bought a wormer or food from the practice. Twenty-two per cent out of nearly 4,000 dogs approached had been recently vaccinated, although the majority of dogs had been vaccinated in the previous year. One per cent of dogs were unvaccinated and one per cent had unknown vaccine status."

Data analysis

All collected data were then entered into a computer database and analysed. "The results clearly indicated that there was no temporal association between vaccination and ill health, nor did we find any association between the number of booster vaccines and ill health," suggested Dr Edwards.

16

"Sixteen per cent of the dogs had signs of ill health recorded by their owners. This may seem high, but the owner-recorded signs varied from very minor such as bad breath, changes in behaviour or a slight limp through to very serious, such as cancer or fitting."

This paper is unlikely to diminish the voice of the dissenters, according to Mr Grimmett. He insisted that *"out of the several million doses of vaccine we've sold in the last few years, we've had very few adverse reactions reported, but we will always investigate.*

"You get people saying 'I had my puppy vaccinated and he dropped dead the next day'. Subsequently, we do a post-mortem and find it had a congenital health failure, but the owner goes away thinking their pet might have soldiered on with this CHF if it hadn't been for the vaccine. It's a very emotive subject - vaccines can do incredibly destructive things if you believe what some people say."

He added: *"The problem is that it is impossible to prove a negative, and as soon as someone says 'there is a problem with vaccines' and you try and argue the point they'll say 'can you prove there isn't?' Of course you can't."*

All medical interventions, even the humble aspirin, come with the risk of an adverse reaction, yet *the POOCH study found **none***. There are, however, official, government-backed vaccine damage compensation schemes for the parents of children who are damaged by vaccines. This means that vaccine reactions are acknowledged at government level. The parents of vaccine damaged children have to prove, in the UK at least, that their child is at least 80 percent damaged (i.e. there has to be quantifiable evidence that the child has had 80 percent of its life ruined) before any money will be paid out. It's not easy to get compensation when your life has been ruined by vaccines.

As an example, the British Committee on Safety of Medicines stated, following a mass vaccination campaign in 1994, when seven million children were vaccinated in the national measles/rubella campaign: 'Serious reactions to the vaccine were very rare.' The Committee did however admit that 530 serious reactions had been reported. The parents of damaged children who had formed various action groups cited examples in the JABS summer newsletter to illustrate that children had been paralysed and severely disabled for life by vaccines, but they were not considered to be damaged enough to receive compensation from the Vaccine Damage Payment Unit.

Even so, millions and millions of pounds have been paid out to even more severely damaged children on a worldwide basis.

There are also many, many published studies to show that vaccines can cause autoimmune diseases, arthritis, brain damage, diabetes, thyroid disease, allergies, skin problems, bleeding into the brain, cancer, mobility problems, tissue damage, and more.

The Merck Manual states that, 'children should not be given the DTP vaccine again if a child develops encephalopathy within 7 days; a convulsion within 3 days; persistent, severe, inconsolable screaming or crying for three hours or an unusual, distinctive, high-pitched cry within 48 hours; collapse or a shock-like state within 48 hours, and immediate severe or anaphylactic (allergic) reaction to the vaccine'. This is a direct admission from a vaccine manufacturer that these events can follow administration of a vaccine.

The Animal Health Trust, however, could find no evidence whatsoever that there are any adverse effects to vaccines in dogs. It may, perhaps, be worth asking yourself the question, 'are canine vaccines safer than human vaccines?'. If this is the case, then why is the safer technology not transferred to the human sphere?

The Animal Health Trust (AHT) research was billed, by the Animal Health Trust, as *independent*. It worries me that an organisation such as this can claim to be independent, and no-one will challenge the claim (and those who do are called contentious). The AHT is a registered charity which, amongst other things, develops vaccines. The study itself was funded by the National Office of Animal Health (NOAH), the trade association which represents the manufacturers of veterinary vaccines and other drugs in the UK. In 2002, NOAH's members accounted for well over 90 percent of the £389 million UK animal health market. NOAH paid the Animal Health Trust £30,000 for a successive number of years in order to conduct the research which found that there are no adverse events in dogs in the three months following vaccination. This research was sponsored because Canine Health Concern's research showed that there are adverse events in the three-month post-vaccine period.

Even revered veterinary publications reported that a study looking into vaccine side-effects, conducted by an organisation that develops vaccines, and funded by an organisation representing vaccine manufacturers, was *independent*.

18

Perhaps I am guilty of misunderstanding the word, 'independent'? I looked the word 'independent' up in the dictionary, just to be sure that I wasn't mistaken in suspecting that there might be an inbuilt bias with the POOCH study.

Independent: not dependent or relying on others; not subordinate; completely self-governing; not affiliated or merged with a larger organisation; thinking or acting for oneself; not subject to bias; having or affording a comfortable livelihood without necessity of working or help from others; not depending on another for its value.

Now, if you care to take a look at the Animal Health Trust web site or report and accounts, you'll see quite a few requests for funding, and taking money from industry isn't uncommon for the AHT. In fact, the AHT has research facilities for hire, especially where the vaccine industry is concerned. It also develops its own vaccines (a canine distemper vaccine being one example). There's nothing wrong with this. The Animal Health Trust and NOAH are in the business of developing and marketing vaccines, and funding is required in order to do this.

However, the Animal Health Trust, and its sponsors – the UK veterinary vaccine industry – both have a vested interest in proving their belief that vaccines don't cause harm. I personally would expect the professionals concerned, the vets and journalists, to question the independence claim, and not simply to accept it on face value. Instead, I receive emails of the sort shown below:

Dear Catherine

I was recently browsing your website, and found that you have omitted to mention the most comprehensive and rigorous independent study yet performed in the UK on adverse vaccination reactions in dogs. For your convenience I have included a link to the press release so you can add it to your site at your earliest convenience: http://www.noah.co.uk/pressrel/2004/20040402a.htm

I trust it's omission was an oversight and that a passionate, independent researcher such as yourself would not ignore the findings because they don't agree with your own?

Yours sincerely, a vet

19

You will find that I don't include individuals' names when the inclusion of the name might cause embarrassment for the person concerned. My aim is not to shame anyone, or to put them in a bad light, but to examine what is true or not true about animal healthcare. This vet clearly believes that the Animal Health Trust's research, sponsored by the vaccine industry, is independent. When I see emails or letters like this, I wonder for a second whether I'm John Nash, the subject of the film, *A Beautiful Mind*, seeing things that just aren't there. You, however, are free to go to the AHT website and draw your own conclusions from their research.

I wrote to another vet who I admire greatly, asking, 'What are your views on the vaccine industry sponsoring research to say that vaccines do not cause adverse reactions?' The reply:

'There's no difference between the target industry doing any basic or clinical research in their field of commerce. It happens everywhere. Even if the research doesn't emanate from the company per se, many prominent and fledgling scientists and clinicians (physicians and allied health professionals - dentists, podiatrists, vets, nurses etc) are supported by companies to do research, sponsor their talks and travel at meetings, given free tickets and meals etc. So, it's all biased even when someone truly believes they aren't influenced - it's subliminal. This is BIG business. But, without industrial support for these endeavours, much would never get done, as there's not enough public money or infrastructure to pay for it without the private sector's support.'

So it's accepted within the healthcare professions that industry sponsors research, and it's felt that nothing much would get done without this funding. The trouble is, in my honest and humble opinion, this also means that we have to ask whether the research can be accepted on face value. We wouldn't have to ask this question if the research were truly independent.

Or maybe I am wrong, and maybe the CHC survey is wrong. Maybe the Animal Health Trust is right: vaccines are harmless. It's possible, of course.

It is here that we get back to the sphere of belief. Those of us who must make decisions about our animals' healthcare have to sift through the words, and other people's beliefs, in order to ascertain the right thing to do. John Bradshaw, author of *Bradshaw on the Family* wrote:

'As we humans act in repetitious ways, necessitated by circumstances relating to survival, these repetitions become habitual.

These habitual behaviours soon become socially acceptable ways of behaving. They are socially agreed upon. After a while these socially agreed upon habitual ways of behaving become what sociologists term 'legitimised'. After being legitimised for a while, they become unconscious. The unconscious legitimisations gradually evolve into *laws of reality*. We no longer question them. We accept them: they are predictable. They insure our security. If someone tries to change them, we get very upset.

'In fact they are not reality at all. As cultural anthropologists have continuously pointed out, other cultures do things quite differently. The laws of reality that emerged from our legitimised habits are actually a 'consensus reality'. The 'consensus reality' is what we've all agreed on as constituting reality.'

My question is: what is reality in relation to pet vaccination? Are vaccines safe, as the Animal Health Trust and NOAH tell us? Or do they have the potential to harm our pets? Can we rely upon 'proper' scientific research, conducted in a 'proper' way, by 'properly qualified' individuals, or do animal guardians have a right to ask questions, and the right to answers, that will empower them to make informed choices for themselves?

In '*What Vets*' I included many case stories of dogs who appeared to have been vaccine damaged. These were discounted by some on the basis that they were 'anecdotal'. This time I'm going to explain the possible side-effects of vaccines another way – by simply listing the scientific research and, where I feel it necessary, explaining the implications of that research.

It is your duty, and your privilege, to put your existing beliefs aside or, if you have no beliefs because you've been relying on the 'experts' so far, it is your duty and privilege to think for yourselves. Examine the following research, and see what you conclude.

Two
The Science Available on Vaccine Reactions

The Vaccine Research Group at the Purdue University School of Veterinary Medicine conducted several studies to determine if current vaccines cause changes in the immune systems of dogs that might lead to life-threatening immune mediated diseases. They obviously conducted this research because concern already existed. Their findings were published in 1997. The dogs were vaccinated using a typical schedule used for pet dogs and closely followed for three years with blood and other tests at regular intervals.

The blood of all the vaccinated dogs were seen to contain significantly elevated concentrations of antibodies directed against proteins that are present in commercial vaccines as contaminants of the production process. None of the unvaccinated control dogs had similar increases in these antibodies. The contaminant proteins were typically of bovine (cow) origin, since foetal calf serum is used as a component in the growth media used to grow viruses for vaccine production.

Dog proteins and cow proteins are very similar in structure, and the Purdue team felt that antibodies produced by the vaccinated dogs might have cross-reacted with the dogs' own tissue proteins in a 'process similar to autoimmunity'. The team added that experiments in other animal species suggested that the antibodies might eventually cause diseases in the vaccinated animals.

The Purdue study indicates that vaccines might trigger dogs to attack their own biochemicals, potentially (but not definitely) causing a range of immune-mediated diseases, some of which you may have seen in your own animals. Immune-mediated diseases include:

Hashimoto's thyroiditis – inflammation of the thyroid gland involving the production of autoantibodies to thyroglobulin. Clinical signs include obesity and coldness, thinning coat, baldness, and autoimmunity in joints, muscles and the liver.

Addison's disease – atrophy of the adrenal cortex, probably as an autoimmune response. Clinical signs include vomiting, diarrhoea, anorexia, lethargy and collapse. Please note that whenever the word 'autoimmune' is used, it denotes that the individual's own body is attacking itself.

Rheumatoid arthritis – a form of arthritis in which there is inflammation of a joint with progressive erosion of cartilage and bone, eventually leading to lameness or severe deformity. Again, the inflammation is a symptom of autoimmunity, where the individual's body is attacking itself.

Systemic Lupus Erythamatosus (SLE) – an autoimmune disease characterised by inflammation and destruction of tissues. Clinical signs are varied, but a common feature is the presence of a number of autoantibodies. Other common symptoms include platelet deficiency (meaning the blood will not clot when required) and inflammation in blood vessels, joints, skin, nervous system and thyroid. Most canine autoimmune disorders may appear as part of the SLE complex, including haemolytic anaemia, lameness, nephritis (inflammation of the kidney), and bleeding into the skin.

Idiopathic thrombocytopenic purpura – a reduction in platelets in the blood leading to bleeding into the skin.

Haemolytic anaemia (also called Autoimmune Haemolytic Anaemia, AIHA, and Immune Mediated Haemolytic Anaemia, IMHA) – destruction of the red blood cells, usually by the action of autoantibodies. The disease can lead to death within days, and is an acknowledged vaccine reaction in both dogs and humans.

Chronic active hepatitis – a longstanding inflammatory condition of the liver. There may be an autoimmune reaction against the individual's own hepatocytes (liver cells).

Diabetes mellitus – inadequate insulin production. Genetic makeup appears to be a factor, although an autoimmune response may be involved in Type I disease. Without treatment, this condition leads to coma and death.

Hypogonadism – decreased function of the testis and ovary which may be due to lesions in the testis and ovaries, hypothalamus or pituitary gland.

Myasthenia gravis – an autoimmune disease in dogs in which the muscles of the body rapidly become fatigued on exercise, due to a failure of the neuromuscular junction.

Pemphigus, vitiligo - skin inflammations which are autoimmune in nature.

Glomerulonephritis – a condition of the kidney, usually due to the deposition of immune complexes. Clinical signs are of acute kidney failure.

Alopecia – the absence of hair from areas where it is normally present, which can be caused by viruses, bacteria, fungi, parasites, poor nutrition, allergy, endocrine imbalances or autoimmunity.

Grave's disease – the leading cause of hyperthyroidism, Grave's disease represents a defect in the immune system, causing production of autoantibodies which attack the thyroid gland and cause overproduction of thyroid hormone.

Hypoparathyroidism – atrophy of the parathyroid glands leading to a dangerous drop in blood calcium levels and potential death.

Seizures and other neurological manifestations.

Uveitis (inflammation of the eye) and other immunologic eye diseases.

In all of these autoimmune diseases we see three main factors:

1.   Individuals attack their own biochemicals, leading to destruction of cells, blood components and/or organs, and/or

2.   Inflammation and/or

3.   Atrophy (a decrease in size or wasting away of organs or tissue).

In short, what we are seeing with autoimmunity is a reaction within the immune system which either turns bodily functions off, or over-stimulates bodily functions.

Dr Jean Dodds wrote: 'Immune-suppressant viruses of the retrovirus and parvovirus classes have recently been implicated as causes of bone marrow failure, immune mediated blood diseases, haematological malignancies (lymphoma and leukaemia), dysregulation of humoral and cell-mediated immunity, organ failure (liver, kidney), and autoimmune endocrine disorders, especially of the thyroid gland (thyroiditis), adrenal gland (Addison's disease), and pancreas (diabetes). Viral disease and recent vaccination with single or combination modified live virus vaccines, especially those containing distemper, adenovirus 1 or 2 and parvovirus, are increasingly recognised contributors to immune-mediated blood diseases, bone marrow failure, and organ dysfunction.'

The Purdue study was but one further piece in the jigsaw to confirm Dr Dodds' research.

Dr Dodds is suggesting that both viruses and the tools we use to prevent the contraction of viruses – vaccines – can cause a whole range of life threatening illnesses including bone marrow failure, blood-borne cancers, and organ and endocrine failure.

The Significance of the Purdue Study

The biochemicals seen to be under attack in the Purdue study included fibronectin, laminin, DNA, albumin, Cytochrome C, cardio-lipin and collagen.

What is the significance of this?

Fibronectin is an 'extra cellular adhesion molecule' involved in tissue repair; embryogenesis (embryogenesis is a developmental process that usually begins once the egg has been fertilized. It involves multiplication of cells and their subsequent growth, movement, and differentiation into all the tissues and organs of a living organism); blood clotting, and cell migration/adhesion. Vaccines potentially cause dogs to attack the biochemical involved in these functions.

Vaccines have also been shown in the Purdue study to stimulate the production of antibodies against laminin. Laminin surrounds muscles, nerves and fat, and has been found to be involved in many cellular activities, including the adhesion, spreading, differentiation, polarisation, proliferation, and movement of cells. Vaccines therefore appear to cause the development of autoantibodies to remove the natural intelligence of cells.

Vaccines also stimulate the production of antibodies against albumin. Albumin is a protein manufactured by the liver which enables fluid to remain in the blood stream rather than leak out into the tissues. If albumin gets very low, fluid build up and inflammation can occur in the body. Importantly, important nutrients - fatty acids - are carried with the aid of albumin to cells in the body. Fatty acids are the building blocks for lipids, which form all of the membranes around and inside cells. Fatty acids are essential for life, and albumin is essential for their distribution. Without albumin, a body simply doesn't get the nutrients it needs to sustain health, and internal boundaries are impaired.

Antibodies against Cardiolipin were also found in the Purdue study. Anti-Cardiolipin autoantibodies (ACA) are frequently found in patients with systemic lupus erythematosus (SLE). They are also found in patients with other autoimmune diseases, as well as in some individuals with no apparent previous underlying diseases. Elevated levels of ACA have been reported to be significantly associated with the presence of both venous and arterial thrombosis (blood clots within the heart or blood vessels), thrombocytopenia (a reduction in the number of platelets in the blood leading to poor blood clotting, haemorrhage, and bleeding into the skin), and recurrent foetal loss, as well as neurological conditions.

Vaccinated dogs, but not the non-vaccinated dogs, were also shown to develop autoantibodies to Cytochrome C in the Purdue study.

Cytochrome C is a protein that is important in the process of creating cellular energy. Cytochrome C is part of the cascade of cellular events that lead to programmed cell death (apoptosis) when cells are damaged. Insufficient or excessive cell death can contribute to disease, including cancer and degenerative disorders.

Imbalances of Cytochrome C also contribute to Cytochrome C Oxidase Deficiency, so far thought to be an inherited metabolic disorder. Deficiency of Cytochrome C Oxidase may be limited to the tissues of the skeletal muscles or may affect several tissues, such as the heart, kidney, liver, brain, and/or connective tissue; in other cases, it may be systemic.

The disorder may be characterized by a generalised weakness of skeletal muscles, abnormalities of the heart and kidneys, and/or

26

abnormally high levels of lactic acid in the blood (lactic acidosis). Other forms of Cytochrome C Oxidase deficiency are characterised by progressive degeneration of the brain and dysfunction of other organs of the body including the heart, kidneys, muscles, and liver. Symptoms may include loss of previously acquired motor skills, loss of appetite, vomiting, irritability, and/or seizures.

The Purdue study also found that vaccinated dogs were developing autoantibodies to their own collagen. About one quarter of all of the protein in the body is collagen. Collagen is a major structural protein, forming molecular cables that strengthen the tendons and vast, resilient sheets that support the skin and internal organs. Bones and teeth are made by adding mineral crystals to collagen. Collagen provides structure to our bodies, protecting and supporting the softer tissues and connecting them with the skeleton.

If vaccines cause dogs to develop autoantibodies to attack their own collagen, then what sort of illnesses might we expect to arise? Think of all the drugs the pharmaceutical companies will be forced to make available to those whose musculoskeletal system is damaged as a result of vaccines – although, as yet, we don't actually know that this will be the case. All we know is that vaccines caused the Beagles to develop autoantibodies to their own collagen.

Perhaps most worryingly, the Purdue study found that the vaccinated dogs – but *not* the non-vaccinated dogs – were developing autoantibodies to their own DNA.

Deoxyribonucleic acid (DNA) is a nucleic acid which carries genetic instructions for the development of all cellular forms of life and many viruses. DNA is sometimes referred to as the molecule of heredity as it is inherited and used to propagate traits. During repro-duction, it is replicated and transmitted to offspring.

Every living thing starts life with some genetic mutations, inherited from parents. However, mutations can also be acquired during a lifetime. Some occur during cell division; others occur when DNA is damaged by environmental factors, including UV radiation, chemicals and viruses. We now know that vaccines can generate antibodies which attack DNA.

Some mutations appear to cause no harm at all. Others cause disease. One must wonder, then, what the consequences might be when vaccines stimulate antibodies against our dogs' own DNA. Are we shooting genetic faults in through the needle? The thing is, we don't know. All we know is that vaccinated dogs in the Purdue study developed autoantibodies to their own DNA.

According to Cambridge Life Sciences, antibodies directed against native DNA were first detected in the serum of patients with systemic lupus erythamatosus (SLE) in the 1950s. The presence of anti-DNA autoantibodies is one of the four highly specific serological markers included in the 1982 American College of Rheumatology criteria for the classification of SLE. The more of these antibodies an individual has, the higher the disease activity. Long term risks include renal (kidney) and central nervous system involvement.

SLE keeps coming into the picture. The Oxford Concise Veterinary Dictionary describes SLE thus:

'**Systemic lupus erythamatosus (SLE)** An autoimmune disease of unknown cause characterised by inflammation and destruction of a variety of tissues. SLE is frequently reported in dogs and more rarely in other veterinary species. The clinical presentation is varied but a common feature is the presence of a number of autoantibodies, in particular antibodies to nucleic acid. The damage to tissues is mediated by the antibody, either by the activation of complement or by the formation of antibody-antigen complexes, involving such antigens as nucleic acid or tissue protein.

'Canine autoimmune haemolytic anaemia, which also occurs in isolation, can form part of the SLE syndrome. The other common manifestations are platelet deficiency and inflammation in blood vessels, joints, skin, peripheral nervous system, meninges, and the thyroid. It seems that most canine autoimmune disorders may appear, in different combinations, as part of the SLE complex. The commonest presentation is of haemolytic anaemia, lameness, nephritis (inflammation of the kidney), and platelet deficiency leading to purpura (bleeding in the skin). The signs may occur together or sequentially.'

The Oxford Concise Veterinary Dictionary states that the cause of SLE is unknown. We seem to have at least one potential cause for SLE now: vaccines, since vaccines are shown to stimulate antibodies to a number of biochemicals, some of which are implicated in SLE. Secondly, we also know that autoimmune haemolytic anaemia, part of the SLE picture, is an acknowledged vaccine sequel. This was

28

confirmed officially by the British government's working group looking into canine and feline vaccines.

Already we have two sources: Purdue University and Dr Jean Dodds, who say that vaccines can cause autoantibodies which are associated with autoimmune diseases. There are, in fact, many more sources of information about vaccine damage, with significant information coming from Merck, which is one of the world's largest vaccine manufacturers.

The trouble with the Purdue study, however, is that we don't actually know what happened to the vaccinated dogs long-term. The study didn't follow them up. We cannot therefore assume that the autoantibodies found in the Purdue study will lead to autoimmune disease.

Autoimmune disease

Other pieces of research, however, do tell us that vaccines might cause autoimmune diseases. The Merck Manual states: 'Autoimmune diseases may be initiated by the encephalitis that can follow rabies vaccination in which an autoimmune cross-reaction probably is initiated by animal brain tissue in the vaccine'. This means that vaccines can stimulate an inflammatory reaction (specifically here involving the brain), and this inflammatory reaction can lead to a disease in which the animal's own biochemical attack the animal's body.

Rabies vaccine is not common in the UK, but other vaccines are also cultivated on animal brain tissue, and autoimmune diseases in animals are common in the UK. Indeed, the Purdue study appears to show something that was already known and expressed by Merck. Vaccines, whether they are cultivated on brains or not, create an inflammatory response that can lead to autoimmune diseases.

My own edition of the Merck Manual, from which the above quote is taken, is at least ten years old. In short, we have known for at least ten years that vaccines can cause autoimmune disease. The crazy thing is that there are no studies, in humans or animals, to tell us what happens in the long term after an individual is vaccinated. The long-term effects of vaccines are simply not known. Even the Purdue study stopped short. The dogs were rehomed at the age of four and, since

29

most of the new owners would have continued with the vaccine programme, it wasn't thought valuable to continue with the study.

So we know that vaccines cause dogs to attack their own biochemicals. We also know that we don't know the implications of this: no-one has done the research to find out.

Dr Glickman, who led the Purdue study, wrote to me, saying, 'You and I both know that vaccines are not completely safe. We will shortly provide some scientific evidence of just how often vaccines are followed by immune mediated events. My fear however, is that those individuals who want zero risk in their lives will use the information we provide to serve their campaign to eliminate all vaccines from the market.'

Dr Glickman also told me: 'We have just completed the largest veterinary vaccine safety study ever done in which we looked at adverse events for the 30 day period following vaccination. This involved over 3 million vaccinations and included the following adverse events: allergic reactions, analphylaxis, autoimmune haemolytic anaemia, ideopathic thrombcytopenic purpura, etc. We hope to submit at least 3 papers for publication by the end of the year and will present some of our findings at the AVMA yearly meeting in Minneapolis in July 2005. We do not plan to release any preliminary results before the AVMA meeting.'

Dr Glickman clearly believes that the benefits of vaccines outweigh the risks. But he does not claim that there are no risks. I personally feel I must respect the view of someone like Larry Glickman. However, I am interested in knowing who is most at risk. It is clear that not all animals develop autoimmune diseases following vaccination. Dr Glickman's research, due out in 2005, may clarify the numbers – but it doesn't explain why three of my dogs experienced what appear to be vaccine reactions, and why other dogs don't. It doesn't tell me if, should I vaccinate Edward or Daniel, they might be amongst the unlucky ones; whether I will have to watch them die as a result of something I did to them. It's not an easy choice, is it.

Merck states that autoimmune diseases can follow on from encephalitis (inflammation of the brain), which Merck acknowledges can be caused by vaccines.

Further, the Merck Veterinary Manual confirms that modified live parvovirus vaccines are suspected to cause autoimmune haemolytic anaemia in dogs (an autoimmune disease).

Tizards Veterinary Immunology, 4th edition, states that autoimmune haemolytic anaemia may be associated with obvious stress such as vaccination using modified live virus, viral disease, or hormonal imbalances such as pregnancy or pyometra.

The Journal of Veterinary Internal Medicine, Vol 10, No 5 (September October) 1996, published a paper entitled 'Vaccine Associated Immune Mediated Haemolytic Anaemia (IMHA) in the Dog'. The paper states, "This study provides the first clinical evidence for a temporal relationship of vaccine-associated IMHA in the dog."

The study adds: "Because vaccine components can remain in the body for extended periods of time, chemical reactions caused by these vaccine components may continue to occur later than with other drugs that are excreted or metabolised more quickly". It also states that, "Vaccine-associated IMHA has been reported after diphtheria-pertusis-tetanus vaccination in children".

The authors concluded that, because not all cases are reported to the manufacturers (none of the cases in their study had been reported), the prevalence of vaccine-associated IMHA is likely to be under-estimated.

It should be noted that autoimmune haemolytic anaemia is a terrible disease that can kill in a matter of days. It is not nice to see.

Of particular interest to NOAH and the Animal Health Trust, perhaps, is the fact that the study showed a marked difference in frequency of IMHA (also known as AIHA) between the first month after vaccination and subsequent months which was not seen in the control group. 'This temporal relationship strongly supports that vaccination can trigger IMHA in dogs. Although reactions are frequently reported to vaccine manufacturers these companies consider this to be proprietary information and are hesitant to release such data'.

The Merck *Veterinary* Manual states:

'Bone marrow suppression with transient (21 day) or chronic/latent erythroid dysplasia in the presence or absence of thrombocytopenia and neutropenia, Coombs' positive haemolytic anaemia, and immune-mediated thrombocytopenia have been associated with (i.e., may prove to be caused by) both retroviral and parvoviral infections in man and other species. Also, modified live parvovirus vaccines in dogs . . . are suspects as causes (in genetically susceptible animals) of such haematological diseases.'

Translation: autoimmune diseases might be caused by the parvovirus vaccine (as well as the rabies vaccine).

Another source confirming that vaccines can cause autoimmune disease came via an admission on a datasheet accompanying the Rabdomum rabies vaccine, which stated: 'Because Rabdomun is produced on an established cell line, it has safety advantages over inactivated brain-origin rabies vaccines. Tissue-origin vaccines contain extraneous protein in addition to rabies antigen that can lead to autoimmune disease.' Actually, a wide spectrum of vaccines are cultivated on animal tissue – dog, cat, monkey, hamster, and other species' brains, kidneys and tissues. The presence of 'extraneous protein' is an inherent part of the vaccine process, and these proteins, as demonstrated very clearly in the Purdue study, can trigger antibodies which can, potentially, trigger autoimmune diseases. The adjuvants in vaccines can also, as we shall see later, trigger an inflammatory response leading to autoimmune disease.

But *who* is at risk?

Arthritis

We found some worrying correlations between vaccine events and the onset of arthritis in our 1997 survey. Our concerns were compounded by research in the human field.

The New England Journal of Medicine, for example, reported that it is possible to isolate the rubella virus from affected joints in children vaccinated against rubella. It also told of the isolation of viruses from the peripheral blood of women with prolonged arthritis following vaccination.

A paper appearing in *British Veterinary Journal* (May 1995, Bell, Carter, May and Bennett) states that dogs with rheumatoid arthritis showed higher anti-heat shock protein antibody levels in their sera and synovial fluids compared to control dogs. There was a significant correlation between anti HSP65 and antibodies to the canine distemper virus, and they discussed the relevance of the presence of canine distemper virus within the joint. Since vaccines contain modified live distemper virus, this research should be of concern to those who must decide whether to vaccinate their pets.

Then, in 2000, research showed that polyarthritis and other diseases like amyloidosis (which affects organs) in dogs were linked to combined MLV vaccines (*Am Coll Vet Intern Med*, 2000; 14: 381). The CHC survey had already shown the link between arthritis and vaccines, later research confirmed it.

In short, vaccination can lead to arthritis.

Brain and Central Nervous System damage

The Merck Manual – the doctor's bible – is written by Merck, which is a multi-national vaccine manufacturer. As stated previously, Merck acknowledges in its manual that vaccines (i.e., its own products) can cause encephalitis: brain inflammation/damage. In some cases, encephalitis involves lesions in the brain and throughout the central nervous system. Merck describes encephalitis as: 'An acute inflammatory disease of the brain due to direct viral invasion or to hypersensitivity initiated by a virus or other foreign protein. . . Secondary encephalitis, usually a complication of viral infection, is considered to have an immunologic mechanism. Examples are the encephalitides following measles, chickenpox, rubella, smallpox vaccination, vaccinia, and many other less well defined viral infections.'

The consequences of brain inflammation are many.

Encephomyelitis has been shown to appear after vaccination (Greene, CE, ed, Appel MJ, *Canine Distemper in Infectious Diseases of the Dog and Cat*, 2nd edition, Philadelphia: WB Saunders, 1998: 9-22). (Encephomyelitis is the same as encephalitis, except that it affects the spinal cord structures as well as the brain.)

Writing in the *Veterinary Record* during 1992 (130, 27-30), AIP McCandlish et al state: "Post-vaccinal encephalitis is a recognised complication of the administration of certain strains of live attenuated canine distemper vaccine (Hartley 1974, Bestetti and others 1978, Cornwell and others 1988)." So now we know that parvovirus, rabies *and* distemper vaccines can trigger autoimmune disease.

But what of the consequences of brain damage? Encephalitis is, after all, a spectrum disease. It ranges from mild, all the way through to death.

Many owners (73.1%) reported in the CHC survey that, when their dogs seemed to develop short attention spans, it was within three months of a vaccine event.

33

Again, 73.1% of dogs with epilepsy/fits first developed this condition within three months of being vaccinated. Epilepsy is listed by Merck as a symptom of encephalitis (which is itself an acknowledged vaccine reaction). In the human field, parents of epileptic children have been awarded compensation through the vaccine damage compensation schemes run in various countries. Sadly, some of the cases were confirmed on autopsy, after the vaccine had killed the children.

According to Sue Alexander, writing in the newsletter of the Society for Companion Animal Studies, epilepsy is the commonest neurological disorder seen in dogs and constitutes a major health problem (Brewer, 199; Berendt, 2002). It is probable that between 30,000 and 366,000 of the 6.1 million dogs in the UK suffer from epilepsy.

We also found that 72.5% of dogs who were considered by their owners to be nervous and of a worrying disposition first developed this personality trait within three months of being vaccinated.

Many owners reported behavioural problems in their dogs, and 64.9% said the problems started within three months of a vaccine event.

Ataxia (unsteady gait), which can be caused by lesions throughout the central nervous system, was shown to occur in 91% of cases within three months of a vaccine event.

Canine Health Concern's study of illnesses arising post-vaccination found, not surprisingly, that 78.6% of dogs with encephalitis were diagnosed within three months of being vaccinated. Vaccines *can* cause inflammation of the brain – Merck has already confirmed this.

According to Braund's Clinical Neurology in Small Animals: Localisation, Diagnosis and Treatment, post-vaccinal canine distemper encephalitis occurs in young animals, especially those less than six months of age. It has been recognized as a disease entity for a number of years and is believed to be associated with vaccination using live virus. The pathogenesis of this disease is unclear (they say). It may result from:

a. insufficient attenuation of the vaccine virus which causes subsequent infection of the CNS,

b. the triggering of a latent distemper infection by vaccination,

c. other vaccine components, or

d. an enhanced susceptibility of the animal (e.g., animals that are immunosuppressed).

There is one report of post-vaccinal distemper in puppies immunosuppressed as a result of canine parvovirus infection. Clinical signs are usually seen within one to two weeks after vaccination. They include anorexia, listlessness, and slight pyrexia. Neurological signs occur one to three days after the onset of these nonspecific signs. Sudden changes in temperament, viciousness (attacking owners, other animals, and inanimate objects), aimless wandering, howling, incoordination, and terminal convulsions may be seen in acute cases of approximately 24 hours' duration. This disorder differs clinically from spontaneous distemper infection in young dogs by an altered personality (viciousness) that is very similar in nature and clinical course to that seen in the furious form of rabies encephalitis.

All of these neurological/central nervous system conditions do, of course, tie in with research conducted by those who are concerned about childhood vaccines, and even the manufacturers of childhood vaccines.

Merck states: 'Symptoms of encephalitis: may be associated with cerebral dysfunction (alteration in consciousness, personality change, seizures, paresis) and cranial nerve abnormalities.'

I'd like to add, for Oliver and other individuals suffering post-vaccinal paralysis, that the word 'paresis' is included above in Merck's list of encephalitis symptoms. Paresis is described as:

'Muscular weakness of neural (brain) origin. It is usually regarded as a state of partial or incomplete paralysis, resulting in a deficit of voluntary movement. Paresis may result from lesions at any level of the descending motor innervation pathway from the brain. It is most commonly associated with serious diseases of the central nervous system, less commonly the peripheral nerves are involved.' The Concise Oxford Veterinary Dictionary then goes on to name the various forms of paralysis, involving one limb, two limbs, all four limbs, or both hindlimbs. Once again, it's worth reminding you that Merck tells us that vaccines can cause encephalitis, and that symptoms of encephalitis include paresis. I have met many cases of paresis occurring immediately after vaccination but science calls them anecdotal and therefore inadmissible.

Interestingly, Dr Jean Dodds has found that dogs brought to her with problems of aggression screen positively for thyroid disease in a high number of cases. Dr Dodds asserts that vaccines are one of the triggers that causes autoimmune diseases in animals, including Hashimoto's thyroiditis. Dr Dodds also states that immune-mediated thyroid disease can be initiated by a vaccine. One must suspect that autoantibodies are causing both thyroid disease and neurological signs.

Rhone Merieux and Mallinckrodt Inc initiated a recall and discontinuation of use of all their vaccines containing distemper products. The vaccines had been associated with a higher than normally expected rate of post vaccinal central nervous system reactions, occurring one to two weeks after vaccination. Problems first began to be reported in January 1995, and extended to nine of their products (JAVMA 12.1.95).

Of particular significance to me was the phrase 'higher than normally expected rate of post vaccinal central nervous system reactions'. This shows, clearly, that this particular vaccine manufacturer (and probably all of them) expect some level of CNS reactions.

Researcher Dr Teresa Binstock has been examining the mechanisms of vaccine damage. She explains that cytokines (chemicals secreted by the body that affect the degree of inflammatory or immune responses) are released in response to vaccination as part of the process by which vaccinations induce antibody formation. Cytokines are indicated by the occurrence of fever and lethargic behaviour.

Cytokines released in this way are causally associated with two other processes, namely edema (fluid retention) within the central nervous system, and clonal expansions of the T-cell and B-cell subsets which have already been activated by antigens from recent processes in the central nervous system. Dr Binstock explains that some B and T cells can be encoded with neuron-derived epitopes (antigenic determinants) subsequent to infection and/or treatment with antibiotics. This may, in some cases initiate further neuronal (brain) damage.

Translation: prior infection and/or antibiotic treatment, followed by vaccination, can lead to biochemical reactions which lead to brain damage. This explains to me why Oliver may have had a neurological reaction to his vaccine at the age of four – he had cut his foot and received antibiotics prior to his booster.

Dr Binstock says: 'Brain regions whose pre-vaccination neuronal damage has been relatively insignificant may, via vaccination-induced clonal expansions, suffer additional damage. In essence, clonal expansion of those T and B cells can cause the cells to cross the blood brain barrier into the brain and induce additional damage.

'Based on the facts that fever is a vaccination reaction experienced by many individuals and that fever and edema are stimulated by similar cytokines, a subset of vaccinated individuals - as a direct result of cytokines release - may be likely to experience both encephalitis (inflammation of the brain) and subsequent encephalopathy.'

Cancer

When the CHC survey was conducted, it was already acknowledged that vaccines can cause cancer in cats at the site of injection. This was later acknowledged by the British government's working group looking into canine and feline vaccination. Vets in America were resorting to vaccinating cats in the tails or legs so they could amputate when cancer appeared, and one of these vets came to the UK to speak at the British Small Animal Veterinary Symposium annual bash some years ago, clearly stating that they were vaccinating cats in their limbs so they could lop them off.

However, CHC also found cancers in dogs' vaccine injection sites – 81.1% with this condition in the survey were diagnosed within the three-month post-vaccine period.

Then, in August 2003, the *Journal of Veterinary Medicine* confirmed our research when it carried an Italian study which showed that dogs, as well as cats, develop vaccine-induced cancers at their injection sites (JVM Series A, August 2003, vol 50, no 6, pp 286-291).

In general, we found more dogs than normally expected developing cancer (not just at injection site) close to the timing of their shots.

As stated previously, vaccines have long been associated with cancer and leukaemia. Dr Jean W Dodds concludes that the incidence of immune- and blood-mediated diseases has increased since the introduction of MLV vaccines.

In the human field, the Salk polio vaccine has been associated with the development of inheritable cancer. This is reported to be due to the fact that monkeys used in the manufacture of the vaccine were contaminated with a wide range of monkey retroviruses which found their way into the vaccine. One of these, SV40, is said to turn off the part of the gene which protects from cancer. Not only have individuals who received the vaccine developed cancer, with SV40 found at their cancer sites, but their children have, too. In a rountable debate in DVM magazine, Dr Jonas Salk was quoted as saying that he would never use monkeys taken from the jungle to develop vaccines on again.

Merck was also said to be looking into the increased incidence of leukaemia in children. The speculation was that it originated from an avian leukosis virus – from the chick embryos that are used to cultivate the measles component of the MMR vaccine.

Epilepsy/fits

As mentioned earlier, epilepsy is listed in the Merck Manual as a possible component of encephalitis (inflammation of the brain). Merck states: 'Noninfectious causes of encephalitides include . . . vaccine reactions: many.' (I take the word 'many' to mean many types of vaccines). Merck also states that epilepsy can be caused by 'CNS (central nervous system) infections (meningitis, Aids, encephalitis …) and also by a foreign serum or drug allergy (vaccines contain serum), or by convulsive or toxic agents.' Vaccines contain a variety of toxic agents such as formaldehyde and heavy metals. Parents of vaccine damaged children have taken this debate to government level in America, seeking the banning of Thimersol – mercury – from childhood vaccines. Remember the term, 'mad as a hatter'? This refers to the fact that hat makers used mercury to line hats with. After a while, they went mad. Mercury is a neurotoxin.

Merck says that any recurrent seizure pattern may be termed epilepsy. 'Convulsions may recur at intervals if there is a permanent lesion or scar in the central nervous system, in which case a diagnosis of epilepsy is made.'

British government research shows that DTP and MMR vaccines can increase the risk of seizure five-fold. *The Lancet* in 1989 reported that one in 400 children given the MMR vaccine will suffer convulsions; in 1995, The Lancet reported that children given the MMR jab were three times more likely to suffer convulsions than those who didn't receive it. It should be noted that the measles and distemper viruses are, to all intents and purposes, the same virus, and that animal vaccines are just as likely to contain mercury as childhood vaccines.

The American Public Health Laboratory Statistics Unit found that the DTP vaccine is responsible for a four-fold increase in seizures (*What Doctors Don't Tell You*, vol 1, no 8).

A paper prepared by AIP McCandlish and team, and published in the *Veterinary Record* during 1992 (130, 27-30) stated, 'Post-vaccinal encephalitis is a recognised complication of the administration of certain strains of live attenuated canine distemper virus vaccine (Hartley 1974, Bestetti and others 1978, Cornwell and others 1988).' The paper described a Labrador bitch who had whelped 10 pups three days before being given a booster vaccine against distemper, adenovirus, parvovirus, parainfluenza and leptospirosis. When the pups were 22 days old, three of the pups started crying, screaming and fitting. Five of the pups were ultimately destroyed. The cause of the nervous disease was found to be canine distemper and the paper suggested that the vaccine rather than a field virus was responsible.

Organ failure

Merck states in its manual for humans that patients with T cell immunodeficiencies, characterised by heart disease, should not receive live virus vaccines.

Merck states elsewhere: 'The autoimmune reaction is normally held in check by the action of a population of specific suppressor T cells. Any of the above processes (which they say includes a foreign antigen such as animal brain tissue in a vaccine), can lead to or be associated with a suppressor T cell defect.' In simple language, vaccines can cause T cell immunodeficiencies, and T cell immunodeficiencies can lead to deterioration of the heart, as well as autoimmunity.

It is worth noting that some of the diseases we vaccinate dogs against attack organs. Viral hepatitis attacks the liver, Parvovirus attacks the heart, distemper attacks the brain. Since vaccines contain live viruses, it should come as no surprise to learn that some vaccinated individuals develop organ failure shortly after vaccination. The CHC survey found that 61.5% of dogs with liver failure in the survey succumbed within three months of their shots. Of those with kidney damage, 53.7% were seen to be damaged within three months of a shot. We found that 39.2% of dogs with heart conditions also developed their conditions within three months of this period. Then add the data from the Purdue study, and it's easy to draw a conclusion as to why tissues and organs should start to deteriorate post-vaccination.

Dr Larry Glickman, professor of epidemiology at Purdue University, wrote to Cavalier breeder Bet Hargreaves in response to her questions about heart disease in Cavaliers, 'Our ongoing studies of dogs shows that following routine vaccination, there is a significant rise in the level of antibodies dogs produce against their own tissues. Some of these antibodies have been shown to target the thyroid gland, connective tissue such as that found in the valves of the heart, red blood cells, DNA, etc. I do believe that the heart conditions in Cavalier King Charles Spaniels could be the end result of repeated immunisations by vaccines containing tissue culture contaminants that cause a progressive immune response directed at connective tissue in the heart valves. The clinical manifestations would be more pronounced in dogs that have a genetic predisposition (although) the findings should be generally applicable to all dogs regardless of their breed.'

Out of respect for Dr Glickman, I will repeat that he still believes that vaccination is better than leaving dogs exposed to viral disease. Out of respect for myself, I have to claim my right to disagree and look at alternatives.

Skin problems

You may not automatically associate skin problems or conjunctivitis with vaccination. Yet research conducted by two scientists named Frick and Brookes shows that dogs who are genetically pre-disposed to develop atopic dermatitis (inherited inflammatory skin problems) didn't develop this inheritable condition if exposed to an allergen before they were vaccinated. But they did develop it when they were *vaccinated before being exposed to an allergen*. They also developed conjunctivitis.

This is but one piece of research to show that genetically predisposed dogs (and other species) can develop vaccine-induced allergies (inflammatory responses). My view is that any form of allergy can be triggered by vaccines in genetically pre-disposed individuals.

Skin problems, generally, are not life-threatening, but animals with oozing hot spots are not healthy animals – and they don't need to suffer in this way. My fear is that animals who have had an inflammatory response to their vaccine may be simply waiting in line for more deadly autoimmune diseases to show themselves: what sort of biochemical changes are taking place, and what is the potential outcome?

You may, perhaps, think that skin problems are an acceptable price to pay if you are protecting your dogs and cats against deadly viral diseases. The trouble is, we are over-vaccinating our animals, and each shot comes with a risks. Why not minimise the risk?

I personally believe that vets are not taking enough notice of contra-indications. The Merck Manual (for humans), for example, cautions that children with, or from families with, B and/or T cell immunodeficiencies should not receive live virus vaccines due to the risk of fatality. All species with immune systems have B and T cells.

Merck lists features of B and/or T cell immunodeficiencies as inhalant allergies, food allergies, eczema, dermatitis, heart disease and neurological problems. It states that we shouldn't give live virus vaccines to people with, or from families with, these immuno-deficiencies, because they might die. Merck aside, the scientific data is available, and has been available for a very long time, to tell us that vaccines can trigger allergies in genetically pre-disposed individuals, and the allergic reaction could be so severe in some cases as to provoke death.

Please note that individuals who are likely to suffer from inflammatory conditions should not receive live virus vaccines. The reason for this is explained most clearly under 'Systemic Destruction and Death', which is the last heading in this chapter.

How many dogs and cats suffer from allergies, skin, heart and neurological problems, but are vaccinated anyway? Your vet needs to be aware of contraindications, so that at-risk individuals are saved the agony of vaccine damage.

Merck also tells us that serum (found in vaccines) can cause Type III hypersensitivity reactions, including a highly inflammatory skin condition involving painful local lesions leading to tissue necrosis (the death of cells); as well as widespread vascular (blood vessel) injury.

Widespread damage

It would be so easy to see what vaccines are doing if the damage occurred in an easily identifiable way: if you prick your thumb with a thorn, and your thumb bleeds, you know the thorn caused the bleeding. I've been saying for the past twelve years that vaccines can cause a whole range of autoimmune diseases, brain damage, behavioural problems, cancer, epilepsy, diabetes, organ failure, skin problems, arthritis and death. This naturally leads some to the conclusion that I'd blame vaccines if a car ran my dog over.

The Purdue study goes some way towards showing the spectrum of diseases that might result from the vaccine process. Other research, quoted above, certainly show us that specific diseases are vaccine-induced. But why should vaccines do all of this?

A plausible answer lies in one paper prepared by Dr Hans Selye entitled '*A Syndrome Produced by Diverse Nocuous Agents*' (Selye H, 1936, *Nature*, July 4 138:32). This was the first piece of work to illustrate the syndrome of a non-specific response to injury.

Selye demonstrated that living organisms have a general non-specific reaction pattern; a general defence mechanism with which they meet damage caused by a variety of potential disease-producers.

Having spent his whole life researching and defining the non-specific stress syndrome, Selye was able to show that disease pathology includes enlarged adrenal cortex; intense atrophy of the thymus, the spleen and all lymphatic structures; signs of petechial bleeding (bleeding into the skin or mucous membrane) – into the lungs, thymus, pericardium and other internal organs and intrathoracic cavity; ulceration of the lining of the stomach and duodenum; disappearance of eosinophil cells (white blood cells produced in the bone marrow); a number of chemical alterations in the constitution of body fluids and tissues; changes in the viscosity and clotting properties of the blood, and signs of derangements in body temperature control (over- or under-heating).

The clinical symptoms of Non-specific Stress syndrome as expressed by Selye, include general feeling of malaise, nausea, coated tongue, reflux (a back flow of liquid against its normal direction of movement), otitis media (ear infection), upper respiratory tract infections, runny nose, sticky eyes, clamminess, rash, tenderness of the liver and spleen, pains and aches in the joints, gastro-intestinal disturbance, diarrhoea and/or constipation.

Selye recognised three states in Non-specific Stress Syndrome:

1. The alarm stage, when the body is acutely affected and mobilises all of its defences and corticoid activity rises sharply;

2. The stage of resistance, when the body is at a maximum capacity to resist the insult and;

3. The stage of exhaustion when all defences have been exhausted and the organism may succumb.

Generally, an animal or human cannot maintain a continuous state of alarm.

According to Selye, if the organism is confronted with an insult so damaging that its normal defence mechanisms are unable to mobilise and complete a healing response, the organism will either sustain chronic damage or respond with death. If the defence mechanisms are not normal, that is, if the organism's immune system is already stressed and dealing with other challenges, chronic or acute disease will result.

In the alarm stage of Selye's Non-specific Stress Syndrome, the cells of the adrenal cortex discharge hormone-containing granules into the blood stream. Under certain conditions, an excess production of the hormone mineralocorticoid desoxycorticosteron (DOC) causes brain lesions. When this is coupled with vascular lesions, also characteristic of Non-specific Stress Syndrome, it may lead to the destruction of large parts of the brain.

Going back to Merck, we know that vaccines can cause encephalitis (inflammation of the brain) and that epilepsy can be a symptom of encephalitis. We also know that Merck advocates a diagnosis of epilepsy when the seizures continue to occur, pointing to lesions in the brain.

Vaccine researchers also discuss demyelination. Charles M Poser of the Harvard Medical School Department of Neurology wrote: 'Almost any . . . vaccination can lead to a noninfectious inflammatory reaction involving the nervous system . . . The common denominator consists of a vasculopathy that is often . . . associated with demyelination.' According to Dr Harris L Coulter, 'a vaccine-associated encephalitis sometime during the first year of life could easily interrupt the myelination process and thus cause neurological damage.'

Myelin is the tough, white, fatty, waterproof substance that coats the nerves like insulation on an electric wire and has the same function. Coulter contends that vaccines can cause inflammatory reactions in the nervous system and interrupt myelination. The result in many cases is encephalitis plus allergic reactions, hypersensitivity, enteritis, autism, dyslexia and other conditions.

Merck says, 'The myelin sheaths of many nerve fibres promote transmission of the neural impulse along the axon. Many congenital metabolic disorders affect the developing myelin sheath. Unless the innate biochemical defect can be corrected or compensated for, permanent, often widespread, neurological deficits result.

'In acute disseminated encephalomyelitis (post infectious encephalitis), demyelination can occur spontaneously, but usually follows a viral infection or inoculation (or very rarely a bacterial vaccine), suggesting an immunologic cause.'

So Merck, who we have to consider the experts where vaccines are concerned, and we also have to acknowledge that Merck is speaking out against its own products, agrees with Coulter (author of *Vaccinations, Social Violence and Criminality*).

A supporting paper appeared in the *Veterinary Record* in 1992: '*Distemper encephalitis in pups after vaccination of the dam, AIP McCandlish, et al*'. Microscopical examination of tissues were made of the pups who contracted distemper after their mother was vaccinated. The post mortem examination revealed a wide range of effects. Pups one and two had depleted lymphoid (B and T cell) tissue in the thymus and spleen, and encephalitis characterised by acute neuronal acidophilia (changes in the brain), or by neuronal degeneration. Post mortem examination of pup three showed marked wasting of the right foreleg, and a small thymus. In the brain, there was severe encephalitis, with mid- and hindbrains severely affected. Small areas of demyelination were present in the hindbrain and the grey matter of the spinal cord. 'No virus could be isolated from the brain, but the results obtained strongly suggested that the vaccinal rather than a field virus was responsible for the syndrome observed.'

Dr Reed P Warren at the Utah State University was quoted in an article in the *Sunday Times* colour supplement in December 1995. He and his colleagues discovered that the measles virus (which is virtually identical, the same virus, as distemper) tricks the immune system into attacking the body's own myelin instead of battling with the virus. If myelin is damaged, the Utah team suggests, this could be the cause of hearing and learning difficulties as well as autism. Meanwhile, the scientist Andrew Wakefield, the most voiceful person linking the MMR vaccine in with autism, has been 'discredited' by those who do not share his *belief*. Scientists in Dublin, incidentally, have isolated components of the MMR vaccine in the guts and brains of autistic children.

Harris Coulter writes, 'A remarkable feature of encephalitis, whether of epidemic origin or due to an infectious disease, traumatic injury or vaccination, is the multifarious diversity of its physical, neurologic, mental and emotional symptoms.' Coulter quotes HH Merritt, emeritus professor of neurology at Columbia University: 'Since any portion of the nervous system may be affected, variable clinical syndromes may occur ... meningeal, encephalitic, brain-stem, spinal cord, and neuritic.'

Diarrhoea, vomiting, flatulence, gastroenteritis, stomach aches, headaches, enuresis, constipation, loss of sphincter control (muscles that surround an orifice), breathing difficulties, hyperactivity, obsessiveness, inattentiveness, mental retardation, seizures, paralysis, aggression, and other conditions are known sequels to encephalitis.

Enuresis is described, incidentally, as the involuntary passing of urine. It is a type of incontinence and is most often caused by stress, but may also be a sign of disease, such as degenerative lesions in the spinal cord (*Oxford Concise Veterinary Dictionary*).

45

According to Coulter, encephalitis is known to produce severe neurological damage in the absence of an acute reaction. As a spectrum disease, this means that you can have any of the above symptoms, such as a headache or stomach ache, or feel slightly queasy, and this cannot simply be passed off as a mild reaction. Other consequences may follow, although *not necessarily*.

Dr JA Morris, an American infectious disease expert declared, 'We only hear about the encephalitis and the deaths, but there is an entire spectrum between fever and death, and it's all those things in between that never get reported.'

Professor R Simpson of the American Cancer Society said that vaccines may cause rheumatoid arthritis, multiple sclerosis, systemic lupus erythamatosus, Parkinson's disease, and cancer. Indeed, people have been saying such things for as long as vaccines have been around. When we have reprogrammed our mental software and thrown out a lot of the received 'scientific' wisdom, perhaps more of us will be able to listen.

Perhaps you will disagree, but when I look at all of this scientific data, I am left in no doubt that vaccines cause autoimmune diseases, allergies, neurological damage, mobility problems, central nervous system damage, skin problems, organ failure, epilepsy, behavioural problems, cancer, and death. It seems, to me, a very high price to pay in order to protect against bacterial and viral disease – especially when there are other ways to mobilise the immune defences. You, of course, have every right to disagree. It's important that you think for yourself, rather than merely absorb other people's assumptions.

Shock to the System

Vaccine manufacturers warn in the data sheets accompanying their products that animals can suffer hypersensitivity reactions following vaccination. Hypersensitivity reactions are essentially allergic or inflammatory responses to the presence of foreign tissues (which are inherent within vaccines). The inflammatory response can be so massive that the animal can die. The name given to cause of death is 'anaphylactic shock'.

A groundbreaking theory that arose in 2004 provides the potential answer, and the reason, why so many of us believe that vaccines are causing widespread harm. You need to sit on the edge of your chair to read this. I think it's important, and that everyone should get their belief systems around this – but, then, belief is so slow to change.

The Possible Answer to Everything!

Open University science student Gary Smith has recently astonished the world of medicine with a theory that some believe could help to cure diseases, including cancer. For me, his theory explains why vaccinating is inherently questionable. For Gary, and others, the theory potentially points towards safer vaccines.

Gary was learning about inflammation as part of his studies when he struck on a hypothesis so extraordinary that it could have implications for the treatment of almost every inflammatory disease – including Alzheimer's, Parkinson's, rheumatoid arthritis, and even HIV and Aids. The theory is so potentially groundbreaking that it is attracting attention from doctors and medical researchers from around the world.

Gary's theory questions the received wisdom that when a person gets ill, the inflammation that occurs around the infected area helps it to heal. He claims that, in reality, *inflammation prevents the body recognising a foreign substance and therefore serves as a hiding place for invaders.* The inflammation occurs when at-risk cells produce receptors called At1 (known as angiotensin II type 1 receptors). While At1 has a balancing receptor (At2) which is supposed to switch the inflammation off, he says that in most diseases this does not happen.

'Cancer has been described as the wound that never heals,' he said. 'All successful cancers are surrounded by inflammation. Commonly this is thought to be the body's reaction to try to fight the cancer, but this is not the case.

'This is the even more exciting bit,' said Gary. 'Infections such as the common cold, the flu, and herpes also cause inflammation. The inflammation is not the body trying to fight the infection. *It is actually the virus or bacteria deliberately causing inflammation in order to hide from the immune system.*'

If Gary is right, then the inflammatory process so commonly stimulated by vaccines is not, as hitherto assumed, a necessarily acceptable sign. It could, instead, be a sign that the viral or bacterial component, or the adjuvant, in the vaccine is winning by stealth.

If Gary is correct in believing that the inflammatory response is not protective, but a sign that invasion is taking place under cover of darkness, vaccines are not the friends we thought they were. They are undercover assassins working on behalf of the enemy, and vets and medical doctors are unwittingly acting as collaborators.

It could be that vaccines are scrambling our animals' biochemical and cellular communications network, sending their defence mechanisms into a state of confusion, leading to inappropriate behaviour. Potentially, vaccines are the stealth bomb of the medical world. Gary's theory makes so much sense when you examine what is known about the immune response and, in the next chapter, the observations of *observant* vets in practice.

The Inflammatory Process

Antibodies are biochemicals within each of us that protect our bodies against foreign invaders such as viruses or bacterins. Class I antibodies serve as markers for white blood cells that attack and destroy body cells which are virus-infected or whose surfaces bear foreign antigens. Type I hypersensitivity reactions are brought about by an antigen reaction with tissue mast cells bearing specific antibodies on their membranes. This releases substances which cause inflammation.

Using a simple analogy, it could be said that the virus is someone who comes along and calls us names. We react in an inflamed manner. By reacting in an inflamed way, we are actually disarming ourselves, and the person who wanted to upset us has succeeded.

The signs of Type I hypersensitivity vary with the species affected, but can include bronchial constriction, diarrhoea, vomiting, salivation, abdominal pain, and cyanosis (a discolouration of the skin and mucous membranes occurring in certain conditions affecting the heart and circulatory system).

In a paper prepared by R Brooks of the Commonwealth Serum Laboratories in the *Australian Veterinary Journal* of October 1991, entitled 'Adverse reactions to canine and feline vaccines', clinical signs of Type I hypersensitivity reactions include restlessness, vomiting, diarrhoea and difficult breathing. He says that some cases can progress to collapse and death.

Class II antibodies govern intercellular co-operation and influence how individuals will react to foreign invaders (antigens) such as a toxin or virus. Class II hypersensitivity reactions can result in tissue injury such as blisters and ulcers to the skin, arthritis, fibromyalgia, and kidney and liver damage. Autoimmune disease is, of course, any disorder involving inflammation or destruction of tissue by the body's own immune system. Type II hypersensitivity reactions include SLE (which is of course life-threatening) and rheumatoid arthritis.

Type IV hypersensitivity reactions cause inflammations. Type IV processes include contact hypersensitivity, autoimmune thyroiditis, and granulomatous conditions (chronic inflammatory lesion in response to foreign invasion *like a vaccine.*)

In short, hypersensitivity reactions are caused by the introduction of a foreign body which leads to the development of antibodies which attack self. When you look at it this way – or at least when I look at it this way – I begin to believe that vaccines, far from helping prevent disease and death, are the biggest group illusion in the history of healthcare. We are simply using vaccines to facilitate the little bugs to win the battle by catapulting them directly into the castle. Vaccines are the SAS, the Marines, the Infiltrators and the Spy Corps all rolled into one – and they're not on our side.

All of the observations of vets in practice in the next chapter, particularly holistic vets who are taught to take a lengthy case history of their patients, indicate that we are simply exchanging full blown viral and bacterial infection with equally deadly but sneakier viral and bacterial damage. We are destroying natural defences and boundaries with the introduction of foreign tissue and other foreign agents.

The scientific community *believes* that vaccines are essentially helpful and, because they *believe* this, we have used vaccines on millions and millions of children and animals. Until Gary Smith came along, no-one even thought, let alone believed, that the immune response might be hiding a virus or bacterin from the body's defence mechanisms, and allowing these pathogens to create widespread damage. This is a terrible concept.

Three
Vets on Vaccines (a different software programme)

Over the past twelve or so years, I have had numerous conversations and correspondences with vets who believe that I am wrong about vaccines. They genuinely believe that vaccines have eradicated epidemics and saved millions of lives. Frequently they tell me that they have looked deeply into the subject and consulted the scientific literature. They often say that they have not witnessed any adverse reactions in practice. Most of the vets you – as the client – will consult will share the view that vaccines are beneficial, and that side-effects are rare.

And yet there are other vets – albeit a minority – who believe that vaccinating is just about the worst thing we can do to our animals. This is despite the education they have received in veterinary college which, on the whole, has presented vaccination as a risk-free and beneficial procedure. Many vets have told me that their education where vaccines are concerned stopped after 'do it', and 'this is how you insert the needle'. Vaccines were just accepted as useful and safe.

And yet, and yet . . . since the introduction of vaccines, there appear to have been medical practitioners who have kept their eyes open and reacted to what their eyes have seen. Cancer specialists, for example, didn't exist before the mass smallpox vaccination programme. Many cancer specialists made direct links to the vaccine, and called for its cessation. Indeed, consider the following obituary for Professor George Dick, carried in *The Guardian* in the late 1990s:

'Professor George Dick, the immunologist who has died aged 82, waged a long war against the vaccination of children for smallpox, which he blamed for killing more victims than the disease.

'By the 1950's smallpox was so rare in Britain that mass vaccination, even with its small risk of mortality, was killing more children than would have died without it. In 1962 Dick spoke out at the British Medical Association annual meeting against the smallpox vaccination programme enjoined by the Minister of Health, Mr Enoch Powell. 'He is asking for a sacrifice of at least 20 babies a year,' Dick said.

'But it was not until 1971 (nine years later), that Sir Keith Joseph, as Secretary of state for Social Services, announced in a letter to all GPs that the government-backed programme encouraging vaccination for children was to be dropped. Dick had made known his opposition to childhood smallpox immunisation to the committee that advised Joseph to drop the programme.

'The other disease with which Dick's name is linked is poliomyelitis. There was a wide and justified fear of the disease in the 1950s, despite the success of vaccines developed by Jonas Salk in 1954. These vaccines were of the dead type, but there were hopes that a live vaccine could be produced which could be taken by mouth instead of by injection. But the danger with early oral vaccines was that the virus might mutate and infect other people with a virulent disease that could lead to death or paralysis.

'In 1956, Dick tried out a new kind of live vaccine on his four-year-old daughter, a decision which he was to report soberly in the British Medical Journal but which caused a flutter of excitement in the tabloid press. But by 1958, after experiments on 200 volunteers, Dick came to the conclusion that the live poliomyelitis vaccines then available were not suitable for use on a large scale, because of the risk of spreading infection.' (The polio vaccine, incidentally, is reported by the World Health Organisation to be the sole cause of polio in America today.)

'In 1962 Dick attacked (on the grounds that the live vaccine could spread the disease) government backing for a change to an oral Sabin live vaccine in place of the Salk vaccine.'

Despite his contentious statements about certain vaccines, George Dick held many prestigious posts. He was a Foundation Fellow at the Rockefeller Institute, a Fellow at the Johns Hopkins University, Professor of Microbiology at Queen's University, and Professor of Pathology at the Middlesex Hospital Medical School.

In essence, Professor Dick spoke out against prevailing views and practices. In doing so, he stood against commercial concerns: wealthy pharmaceutical companies. He had to wait a fairly long time before anyone was prepared to listen and act upon his advice. On some counts, perhaps they never did.

Many in the veterinary field have done the same.

Dr Jean Dodds is an interesting person in so much as she has managed to speak openly about vaccine reactions without incurring the wrath of the scientific community. Her aim, it seems, has always been to bring people with her, rather than wage war with people who have a different view. Her research and her observations have, however, led her to speak out.

She wrote on puppy vaccine schedules: 'While puppies exposed this frequently to vaccine antigens may not demonstrate overt adverse effects, it is clear that their immune systems may still be immature. Consequences in later life may be an increased frequency of chronic debilitating diseases. Many veterinarians trace the present problems with allergic and immunologic diseases to the introduction of MLV (multiple live virus) vaccines some twenty years ago.'

Christina Chambreau DVM says: 'Routine vaccinations are probably the worst thing that we do for our animals. They cause all types of illnesses but not directly to where we would relate them definitely to be caused by the vaccine.'

Martin Goldstein DVM writes in his book, *The Nature of Animal Healing*, 'The links are invisible and, so far, unproven. Even to suggest they exist is to be heaped with scorn from the US medical establishment. Yet a growing number of holistic and now even conventional veterinarians are convinced, from sad experience, that vaccines as they're administered in this country to pets are doing more harm than good. I myself think that's a *conservative* view. I think that vaccines, justly credited as the tamers of disease epidemics, are nevertheless the leading killers of dogs and cats in America today.'

Dr Goldstein talks about pets arriving in his clinic with a history of vaccine-associated symptoms: fever, stiff or painful joints, lethargy, lack of appetite – as if the pet had flu, but it's not the flu. Invariably the owner will admit that the animal was vaccinated a week or two before the symptoms started.

'More subtly,' wrote Dr Goldstein, 'after a week or two, a pet may show other serious symptoms: bleeding gums, enhanced allergies, seizures and haemorrhages. Months, even a year later may come kidney or liver failure, degenerative arthritis, and among other life-threatening conditions, cancer. Are the vaccines to blame? I can't prove that they are. But when I began long ago to suspect the connection and changed my practice accordingly, an amazing thing often happened with those telltale symptoms.

'They began to go away.'

Dr Charles E Loops DVM writes: 'Homeopathic veterinarians and other holistic practitioners have maintained for some time that vaccinations do more harm than they provide benefits. Vaccinations represent a major assault on the body's immune system. Attenuated organisms or chemically killed viruses or bacteria are injected directly into the blood stream, an unnatural route of infection. This profound insult, avoiding the body's first line of defences, and flooding the system with millions of organisms or viral particles, stresses the immune system in a way not of nature's design. This insult causes irregularities and abnormalities in the immune system which then manifests as chronic disease in animals. These chronic diseases range from life-threatening conditions such as auto-immune crises to conditions destroying the quality of life of an animal as in chronic skin allergies.

'What we are now seeing are generations of over-vaccinated animals and these current offspring are suffering the penalty of this medical abuse. In an attempt to control a naturally occurring process of population control and survival of the fittest, the medical establishment has convinced people that mass inoculations are for the good of all, overlooking the health of the individual. Where vaccinations have helped in eradicating or reducing the incidence of severe, acute disease processes, the result has been to plague humanity with more insidious, chronic diseases that are much more difficult to treat and that lower the quality of life for many individual animals and people.'

Dr Donna Starita Mehan writes: 'Routine vaccination, as it is practiced today, is not always effective (especially in the case of the feline leukemia vaccine), and frequently has adverse side-effects, either short or long term. With the use of multivalent (combination: 4 in 1, 6 in 1, etc.) vaccines that are repeated year after year, the frequency and severity of these side-effects in our pets has increased dramatically.

'Not surprisingly, most of the problems involve the immune system. After all, the immune system is what vaccines are designed to stimulate. But they do so in a very unnatural way that can overwhelm and confuse the immune system. The body may overreact to normally harmless substances (allergies, especially flea allergies and other skin problems), or even produce antibodies to itself (autoimmune disease). At the same time, the body may be sluggish in responding to those things that it should reject, such as common viruses, bacteria, fungi, and parasites. This can result in increased susceptibility to acute infections (such as ear infections in dogs, bladder infections in cats), chronic tapeworm problems, or in more degenerative cases, cancer.'

Glen Dupree DVM, writes: 'I do not personally vaccinate my pets, nor have I for many years. There are several reasons for this. From my perspective as a Homeopath, vaccines are among the leading contributors to the psychosis miasm. Some of the signs of psychosis are allergies, bladder disease (cystitis, crystals in the urine, chronic and recurrent problems), behaviour problems (rage, jealousy, fears, restlessness), itchy/draining/waxy ears, food intolerances and inflamed bowels, bronchitis and asthma, arthritis, greasy hair coats, itching, and warts/growths. These symptoms probably sound familiar as they are becoming more prevalent in the pet population.'

Dr Charles E Loops, DVM wrote: 'The first thing that must change with routine vaccinations is the myth that vaccines are not harmful.... Veterinarians and animal guardians have to come to realise that they are not protecting animals from disease by annual vaccinations, but in fact, are destroying the health and immune systems of these same animals they love and care for.'

Dr. Russell Swift, DVM wrote: 'Injected vaccines bypass normal defences. They implant mutated micro organisms, preservatives, foreign animal proteins and other compounds directly into the system. This is done in the name of preventing a few syndromes. If an animal is in an optimal state of health, he or she will produce the strongest immune response possible. This response offers protection against all natural challenges. The irony is that vaccine labels say they are to be given only to healthy animals. If they were truly healthy, they would not need them. Those who are not healthy are the most severely damaged.'

Dr. Pedro Rivera, DVM wrote: 'Vaccinosis is the reaction from common inoculations (vaccines) against the body's immune system and general well being. These reactions might take months or years to show up and will cause undue harm to future generations.'

According to Dr. Pat Bradley, DVM, 'In a general and frightening context, I see the overall health and longevity of animals deteriorating. The bodies of most animals have a tremendous capacity to detoxify poisons, but they do have a limit. I think we often exceed that limit and overwhelm the body's immune system function with toxins from vaccines.'

Dr. Michael Lemmon wrote: 'If an animal already has problems, those problems are contributed to by vaccines. So I don't want to give any more (shots).'

From Dr. Mike Kohn, DVM: 'Unfortunately our society is in the grasp of a health panacea and this panacea is fuelled by the biomedical and pharmaceutical industries. Vaccinations have become the modern day equivalent of leeching. First of all, introducing foreign material via subcutaneous or intramuscular injection is extremely upsetting to the body's defence system. In response to this violation, there have been increased autoimmune disease (allergies being one component), epilepsy, neoplasia (tumours), as well as behavioural problems in small animals. Even though man and animals have been around for thousands of years, interestingly, the increase in cancer, respiratory disorders (most air quality standards are higher today than in decades past), and autoimmune problems have likewise escalated alarmingly during the previous decade. Vaccines are not the only culprit for these increases; however, I feel they are one of the primary offenders.'

Dr. Kristine Severyn, RPH, PhD wrote: 'Vaccines are not always effective, safety is unproven, and long term consequences are unknown. Despite this, the government requires their use, resulting in a lack of incentives for drug companies to produce better products.

'Additionally, mandatory vaccine laws make it impossible to conduct properly controlled studies, so we'll never know if vaccines are truly safe, as is claimed by the government and medical profession. Similar to other procedures, the right of informed consent, i.e. the right to say 'NO', should apply to vaccines.'

Dr. Ana Maria Scholey, DVM says, 'I believe that vaccinations, especially the rabies vaccines, are contributing to a lot of the allergic skin problems seen today, leading to a problem known as vaccinosis, which is characterized by itchy, dark, thickened skin; especially over the abdomen and under the legs. It is seen in both dogs and cats, but is more obvious in the dog.'

Dr. Nancy Scanlan, DVM: 'Every time a dog is vaccinated for parvo, the number of white blood cells in the circulation decreases for a while. This means their immune system won't work as well during that time. Every veterinarian who has been in practice long enough has seen reactions to vaccines, ranging from lethargy, mild fever, sore neck, to vomiting and sleeping for 24 hours, to total collapse and shock. In cats we now recognize that time can cause fibrosarcoma, a nasty cancer. This is officially recognized by the veterinary community, and if this isn't a form of vaccinosis, I don't know what is.'

Doesn't it strike you, as it does me, that all of the above veterinarians are describing Gary Smith's theory: that the inflammatory response – which is expected when you vaccinate - is hiding a virus or bacterin so that it can get in there and cause disease by stealth? That these vets could see something but couldn't tell you exactly why?

In January 2004, the following letter was published in the UK's 'Veterinary Times'. It was the first time in the UK that vets spoke publicly about vaccine dangers.

Dear Editor

We, the undersigned, would like to bring to your attention our concerns in the light of recent new evidence regarding vaccination protocol. The American Veterinary Medical Association Committee report this year states that 'the one year revaccination recommendation frequently found on many vaccination labels is based on historical precedent, not scientific data'.

In JAVMA in 1991, Smith notes that 'there is evidence that some vaccines provide immunity beyond one year. In fact, according to research there is no proof that many of the yearly vaccinations are necessary and that protection in many instances may be life long'; also, 'Vaccination is a potent medical procedure with both benefits and risks for the patient'; further that, 'Revaccination of patients with sufficient immunity does not add measurably to their disease resistance, and may increase their risk of adverse post-vaccination events.'

Finally, he states that: 'Adverse events may be associated with the antigen, adjuvant, carrier, preservative or combination thereof. Possible adverse events include failure to immunise, anaphylaxis, immunosuppression, autoimmune disorders, transient infections and/or long-term infected carrier states.'

The report of the American Animal Hospital Association Canine Vaccine Taskforce in JAAHA (39 March/April 2003)3 is also interesting reading: 'Current knowledge supports the statement that no vaccine is always safe, no vaccine is always protective and no vaccine is always indicated'; 'Misunderstanding, misinformation and the conservative nature of our profession have largely slowed adoption of protocols advocating decreased frequency of vaccination'; 'Immunological memory provides durations of immunity for core infectious diseases that far exceed the traditional recommendations for annual vaccination. This is supported by a growing body of veterinary information as well as well-developed epidemiological vigilance in human medicine that indicates immunity induced by vaccination is extremely long lasting and, in most cases, lifelong.'

Further, the evidence shows that the duration of immunity for rabies vaccine, canine distemper vaccine, canine parvovirus vaccine, feline panleukopaenia vaccine, feline rhinotracheitis and feline calicivurus have all been demonstrated to be a minimum of seven years, by serology for rabies and challenge studies for all others.[4,5,6]

The veterinary surgeons below fully accept that no single achievement has had greater impact on the lives and well-being of our patients, our clients and our ability to prevent infectious diseases than the developments in annual vaccines. We, however, fully support the recommendations and guidelines of the American Animal Hospitals Association Taskforce, to reduce vaccine protocols for dogs and cats such that booster vaccinations are only given every three years, and only for core vaccines unless otherwise scientifically justified.

We further suggest that the evidence currently available will soon lead to the following facts being accepted:

- The immune systems of dogs and cats mature fully at six months and any modified live virus (MLV) vaccine given after that age produces immunity that is good for the life of that pet.
- If another MLV vaccine is given a year later, the antibodies from the first vaccine neutralise the antigens from the subsequent so there is little or no effect; the pet is not 'boosted', nor are more memory cells induced.
- Not only are annual boosters for canine parvovirus and distemper unnecessary, they subject the pet to potential risks of allergic reactions and immune-mediated haemolytic anaemia.
- There is no scientific documentation to back up label claims for annual administration of MLV vaccines.

57

- Puppies and kittens receive antibodies through their mothers' milk. This natural protection can last eight to 14 weeks.
- Puppies and kittens should NOT be vaccinated at less than eight weeks. Maternal immunity will neutralise the vaccine and little protection will be produced.
- Vaccination at six weeks will, however, DELAY the timing of the first effective vaccine.
- Vaccines given two weeks apart SUPPRESS rather than stimulate the immune system.

This would give possible new guidelines as follows:

1. A series of vaccinations is given starting at eight weeks of age (or preferably later) and given three to four weeks apart, up to 16 weeks of age.
2. One further booster is given sometime after six months of age and will then provide life-long immunity.

In light of data now available showing the needless use and potential harm of annual vaccination, we call on our profession to cease the policy of annual vaccination.

Can we wonder that clients are losing faith in vaccination and researching the issue themselves? We think they are right to do so. Politics, tradition or the economic well-being of veterinary surgeons and pharmaceutical companies should not be a factor in making medical decisions.

It is accepted that the annual examination of a pet is advisable. We undervalue ourselves, however, if we hang this essential service on the back of vaccination and will ultimately suffer the consequences. Do we need to wait until we see actions against vets, such as those launched in the state of Texas by Dr Robert Rogers? He asserts that the present practice of marketing vaccinations for companion animals constitutes fraud by misrepresentation, fraud by silence and theft by deception.

The oath we take as newly-qualified veterinary surgeons is 'to help, or at least do no harm'. We wish to maintain our position within society, and be deserving of the trust placed in us as a profession. It is therefore our contention that those who continue to give annual vaccinations in the light of new evidence may well be acting contrary to the welfare of the animals committed to their care.

Yours faithfully

Richard Allport, BVetMed, MRCVS
Sue Armstrong, MA BVetMed, MRCVS
Mark Carpenter, BVetMed, MRCVS
Sarah Fox-Chapman, MS, DVM, MRCVS
Nichola Cornish, BVetMed, MRCVS
Tim Couzens, BVetMed, MRCVS
Chris Day, MA, VetMB, MRCVS
Claire Davies, BVSc, MRCVS
Mark Elliott, BVSc, MRCVS
Peter Gregory, BVSc, MRCVS
Lise Hansen, DVM, MRCVS
John Hoare, BVSc, MRCVS
Graham Hines, BVSc, MRCVS
Megan Kearney, BVSc, MRCVS
Michelle L'oste Brown, BVetMed, MRCVS
Suzi McIntyre, BVSc, MRCVS
Siobhan Menzies, BVM&S, MRCVS
Nazrene Moosa, BVSc, MRCVS
Mike Nolan, BVSc, MRCVS
Ilse Pedler, MA, VetMB, BSc, MRCVS
John Saxton, BVetMed, MRCVS
Cheryl Sears, MVB, MRCVS
Jane Seymour, BVSc, MRCVS
Christine Shields, BVSc, MRCVS
Suzannah Stacey, BVSc, MRCVS
Phillip Stimpson, MA, VetMB, MRCVS
Nick Thompson, BSc, BVM&S, MRCVS
Lyn Thompson, BVSc, MRCVS
Wendy Vere, VetMB, MA, MRCVS
Anuska Viljoen, BVSc, MRCVS, and
Wendy Vink, BVSc, MRCVS

1. Smith, CA (1995) Current concepts - Are we vaccinating too much? JAVMA 207 (4): 421-425

2. Principles of Vaccination (Approved by the AVMA Executive Board April 2001) www.avma.org/policies/ vaccination.htm.
3. Paul, M. S et al (2003) Report of the American Animal Hospital Association (AAHA) Canine Vaccine Taskforce; Executive Summary and 2003 Canine Vaccination Guidelines and Recommendations. JAAHA 39: 119-131.
4. Schultz, Ronald D. Duration of Immunity to Canine Vaccines: What we know and what we don't know. Proceedings - Canine Infectioius Diseases: From clinics to Molecular Pathogenesis, Ithaca, NY, 199, 22.
5. Fisherman, B and Scarnell, J (1976) Persistence of protection against infectious canine hepatitis virus. Vet. Rec. 99: 509
6. Scott, FW and Geissinger, C (1999) Long-term immunity in cats vaccinated with an inactivated trivalent vaccine. Am. J. Vet. Res. 60 (5): 652-8
7. Schultz, Ronald D (2002) Are we vaccinating too much? JAVMA 4: 421
8. Hogenenesch et al (2002) Effect of vaccination on serum concentrations of total and antigen specific IgE in dogs, AJVR 63 (4): 611-616
9. Gorham, JR (1966) Duration of vaccination immunity and influence on subsequent prophylaxis. JAVMA 149: 699-704.

Many of the above signatories, but not all, are homoeopathic vets, and this letter came in the middle of an ongoing attack against homoeopathic vets in the veterinary press. Go back to Chapter One and read the POOCH study press release again. Apart from knocking CHC's vaccine survey, the release (or the report, at least, and the quoted individuals) knocks homoeopaths. Our pets are in the middle of a battle between conventional versus homoeopathic systems of medicine. The POOCH survey does not come out and state its case in its own right; it undermines the values and belief systems of those who would question the safety of vaccines. I find that very interesting.

It happens the other way of course. Many of us who think vaccines are harmful knock not only the science which supports vaccination (which is complicated and takes a long time to explain) but reduce the argument down to one of money: vets are relying on booster income to survive, so they won't make ethical decisions on behalf of our animals. The vaccine industry is big business, and feeds the need for even more drugs to alleviate the damage caused by vaccines, which further boosts the coffers of the multi-billion pharmaceutical industry... and they're nasty swine who will watch us and our pets die before they give up their cosy lifestyles and their power.

Depending upon which side of the fence your belief lies, then you might believe one or the other of the above stories. But what if neither is true? What if there's something else going on? I believe there is.

We only have to look at the terrible diseases we vaccinate dogs, cats and horses against, and we may perhaps see why vaccines are thought to be beneficial. It is understandable that the medical and veterinary professions should applaud vaccines, since it is their mission to eradicate disease. Vaccines hold a wonderful promise. The next question, however, is whether we need to keep repeating the promise.

Four
The Diseases We Vaccinate Our Animals Against

In this chapter, we look at the diseases we are vaccinating our dogs, cats and horses against. However, the considerations given below apply to any vaccine used in any species. In my view, it doesn't matter which virus or bacterin you are vaccinating against, or whether the vaccine is for a dog, cat, rabbit, monkey, ferret or human. Whilst acknowledging that we need to protect ourselves and our animals against viral and bacterial disease, we also need to make choices about the ways in which we proffer protection. We can only make those choices if we understand the issues.

In addition to describing the diseases – which we surely want to help our animals avoid – I am also including information relating to known vaccine side-effects. I share this information because animal guardians don't usually get to see the data sheets or the research material that vets get to see. They tend to rely upon information given by their vet, and I believe that the veterinary profession has a strong bias in favour of vaccines, and a training that causes them to look away from the other view.

This means that animal guardians are being disempowered, unable to make decisions, but able only to do as they are told. Don't you think we should be encouraged to understand what we are doing to our animals in the belief that we are helping them?

In presenting this information, I am deliberately painting a black picture about vaccines – because I *believe* a balance needs to be redressed. Pro-vaccinators will argue that vaccine reactions are very rare. Those of us who choose not to vaccinate (and we are significant in number) believe that vaccine reactions are not rare, but common and barely recognised for what they are. Further, because pet owners mostly get their vet's opinion, and because the veterinary profession has been betrayed by the system that has evolved, most of us who love and care for our animals rarely get to see the full picture.

The jury, then, is still out on how common these reactions are. Further, no-one knows whether your beloved animal is going to be the one who has one of these 'rare' reactions. It is up to you to look at the evidence presented here, and the evidence presented by pro-vaccinators, so that you can make an informed choice about your animals' preventative healthcare. Do not make fear-based decisions.

Make decisions based upon knowledge and understanding. And please don't do anything just because someone told you to.

For those of you interested only in horse or cat vaccines, please also read the information relating to the canine distemper vaccine, as it contains information that applies to all vaccines.

Canine Infectious Diseases

Dogs are routinely vaccinated against:

Distemper

Distemper is a serious contagious, viral disease of dogs, foxes, ferrets and mink. It is characterised by fever, gastro-enteritis, bronchopneumonia, and nervous signs. Symptoms include diarrhoea, vomiting, pneumonia and incoordination. Some strains can cause thickening of the skin of the nose and pads. About half of affected dogs may die.

Some say, thanks to the vaccine programme, that distemper is now a very rare disease. Most vets will tell you that they haven't seen a case in at least ten years; younger vets will never have seen it.

It is difficult to obtain separated vaccines – that is, vaccines for one viral disease only. Intervet's Puppy DP vaccine (for distemper and parvovirus) comes with the following contraindications/warnings: 'Only healthy dogs should be vaccinated. The vaccine may not be effective in dogs incubating the disease at the time of vaccination. In the rare event of a hypersensitivity reaction following vaccination, administer an antihistamine, corticosteroid or adrenaline, without delay and by the most immediate route. Some animals may be immunologically incompetent and fail to respond to vaccination. A good immune response is reliant on the reaction of an immunogenic agent and a fully competent immune system. Immunogenicity of the vaccine antigen will be reduced by poor storage and inappropriate administration. Immunocompetence of the animal may be compromised by a variety of factors, including poor health, nutritional status, genetic factors, concurrent drug therapy and stress.' Intervet recommends boosting for distemper every two years, and parvovirus every year (the company has since marketed vaccines that need boosting every three years).

To explain Intervet's techno-speak, all vaccines are licensed for use in healthy animals (and humans) only. This is why the data sheet for every vaccine product will stipulate, 'for use in healthy animals only'. Modified Live Virus (MLV) vaccines are attenuated (rendered safe!) in the lab, and the virus is designed to multiply over time in the animal, until such time as antibodies are produced to overcome the vaccine challenge. To respond to the vaccine challenge, an individual needs to have a healthy immune system. The immune system is a finite resource: if it is already being used to fight a disease, then there may not be enough immune system left to fight the vaccine challenge. This is one situation in which vaccines cause the disease they are designed to prevent.

For this reason, Intervet cautions that the vaccine may not work if the animal is already unhealthy, or incubating a disease when he is vaccinated. Indeed, the viral component of the vaccine could add to the problem and ensure that the animal succumbs to the disease you are vaccinating against.

In short, vets and animal guardians should take very seriously the advice that unhealthy animals should be spared the vaccine programme. This, in my view, includes animals who are elderly, epileptic, arthritic, under the weather, have raised temperatures or skin problems, or who appear unwell in any way whatsoever.

Intervet also gives vets advice on what to do if the animal has a rare hypersensitivity reaction (anaphylactic shock). Anaphylaxis is described as a Type I hypersensitivity in which damaging changes are induced by the release of histamine. Anaphylactic shock is an extreme allergic reaction which can lead to bronchial constriction, dilation of the veins, circulatory collapse, and possible death. This is why doctors and nurses, who are vaccinated regularly, always have adrenaline on standby at vaccine time. Milder, less life-threatening allergic reactions can also occur post-vaccination.

Intervet counsels that vaccines must be stored and administered correctly. Vaccines can spoil if kept in unsuitable temperatures. They could become ineffective, or they could become contaminated, and so need to be protected from light and heat. Personally, I believe that if you do decide to vaccinate, you should allow your vet to do it, since the vaccine is more likely to have been stored correctly (in America and Ireland pet owners can buy their own vaccines and administer them themselves). Further, if the animal does have an anaphylactic reaction, then at least the vet will be there, with the appropriate resources, to deal with the emergency.

Intervet also tells vets that 'immunocompetence of the animal may be compromised by a variety of factors, including poor health, nutritional status, genetic factors, concurrent drug therapy and stress'. This is, to me, the crux of the matter. It explains why some animals seem unscathed by vaccines, and others are damaged by vaccines. It also indicates that rescue animals should not be vaccinated, since they are likely to be stressed and potentially malnourished. If this is the case, their immunocompetence could result in the vaccine causing the disease we are trying to prevent, and this is how outbreaks occur.

Immunocompetence means the competence of the immune system. If the immune system isn't functioning in a healthy way, then the animal (or human) may:

1.   Be unable to respond to the viral challenge in the vaccine, in which case no immunity will be conferred.
2.   Develop the disease you are vaccinating against (the virus will enter the body unchallenged by the immune system).
3.   Have an abreaction and allergies, or autoantibodies which could lead to autoimmune disease.
4.   Have a massive allergic reaction and die (without the aid of adrenaline etc).

As Intervet and other vaccine manufacturers know, because they say so on their data sheets, the immune system can be unhealthy for the following reasons: there is a genetic fault or faults; the animal is already unhealthy, so his immune system is already being utilised elsewhere to overcome the disease state; if the animal isn't receiving the nutrients he needs, since nutrients feed all of the systems in the body, including the immune system; if the animal is being given drugs to combat existing disease states, such as steroids for inflammatory conditions, which are designed to depress the immune system; and if the animal is under stress – because stress severely depletes specific nutrients and causes the release of biochemicals which then render the animal unable to mount an adequate response to the deliberate stress induced by vaccination (vaccines are designed to stress the immune system and thereby provoke an immune response). There is, in addition, a chapter in this book dealing with the stress response and the effect it has on the immune system.

Parvovirus

Canine Parvovirus is closely related to feline viral enteritis. It causes damage to the heart muscle in puppies below the age of eight weeks of age, and occasionally in older dogs. A high percentage of affected puppies under the age of eight weeks die of heart failure. Only 10% of young dogs over the age of eight weeks will die of the disease. Death is rare in older dogs, and enteritis (diarrhoea) is the main consequence of infection.

Parvovirus didn't exist before 1979. The Oxford Concise Veterinary Dictionary postulates that this new virus was caused by shedding of the feline enteritis vaccine (shedding is where vaccinated animals pee or poo, and vaccine components are consequently sniffed by other animals).

A Sunday Times article quoted scientists who claim that parvovirus was created by a vaccine manufacturer which cultivated the distemper vaccine on cats' kidneys that were infected with feline enteritis. If either explanation is to be believed, parvovirus is a cross-species vaccine-induced disease.

All of the contraindications and warnings (above), given in vaccine company datasheets for the distemper vaccine, also apply to the parvovirus vaccine.

Canine Viral Hepatitis

Hepatitis means inflammation of the liver. Viral hepatitis is a contagious disease of dogs and foxes transmitted through contact with animals with infected urine, or through contact with equipment and pathways/fields contaminated with infected urine.

The principal causes of viral hepatitis in dogs are canine viral hepatitis (adenovirus), the herpes virus, and the parvovirus. The effects of viral hepatitis vary according to the age of the animal or the virus strain, ranging from mild and invisible, to enlargement of the lymph glands and tonsils, severe abdominal pain, and death.

According to the Intervet data sheet, dogs over 12 weeks of age should acquire permanent immunity to contagious hepatitis. All of the contraindications and warnings listed above apply equally to the hepatitis vaccine. Dogs therefore don't need boosting against hepatitis annually, although it's often included in combined vaccines.

The contraindications and warnings listed under 'Distemper' apply here, too.

Kennel Cough

Bordetella - kennel cough - is like the flu: most cases are not life threatening, and they're not much worse than a bad cold. Occasionally bronchopneumonia will be a complication. Parainfluenza, the 'Pi' in combination vaccines, is also referred to as kennel cough. Again, it's generally not fatal.

The disease is mostly treated with throat-soothing remedies, and by keeping the dog quiet.

Because kennel cough is a number of strains of disease (which, like the flu, mutate), the current vaccine is not seen to be terribly effective.

Kennel cough is inconvenient and will take your dog 'out' for a week or two. I've had the flu on occasions and although I can't say it was pleasant, it did give me the chance to lie in bed and rest, and stimulated a renewed vigour and zest for life when it was all over. It also stretched the 'muscles' of my immune system (use it or lose it!).

Kennel cough is only serious when an animal is very elderly or already ill. If a dog has a good immune system (good genes, healthy food, not too much stress), then they're not even going to pick kennel cough up. Edward and Daniel, as nine-month-old puppies, were exposed to kennel cough by my older, vaccinated dogs. Ed and Dan had not been vaccinated but had received the homoeopathic nosode (the vaccine alternative) and they didn't cough once. My dogs who did contract kennel cough recovered well.

The data sheet for the Kavak Parainfluenza vaccine, from Fort Dodge, contains all of the warnings and contraindications as listed for the distemper vaccine: only healthy animals should be vaccinated, in the event of an anaphylactic shock take immediate action, some animals won't respond, etc. Why risk potential death by vaccinating for a disease that isn't generally life threatening?

Of course, this leaves the problem of kennels demanding kennel cough vaccination. It's embarrassing for a kennel, after all, to get a reputation for spreading disease, so they often insist on this vaccine – even though a trial by Christopher Day showed that the homoeopathic alternative, the nosode, can halt an epidemic in a kennel, and a kennel cough vaccine is literally worse than giving the dogs nothing at all. The answer, I suspect, is to make other arrangements and not kennel your dog until the requirements change. It only takes a little will, and it is easy to find a kennel alternative.

Other solutions exist. The British Veterinary Association, working with the environmental health boys, sent guidelines to local councils back in the late 1990s, suggesting that councils shut kennels down if they don't demand proof of annual shots from customers. Perhaps someone in a position of power could do something about this seemingly unlawful, unscientific and potentially harmful requirement, especially in light of duration of immunity studies and COBTA announcements.

Leptospirosis

Lepto is a disease caused by bacterial infection. It can affect humans, cattle, pigs, sheep, goats, dogs, and rarely cats.

There are two types of lepto in dogs, which can cause fever, jaundice, vomiting, loss of appetite, depression and pain in the kidneys. One form attacks only the kidneys, the other attacks the liver and kidneys. Leptospirosis can be contracted through contact with an infected animal's urine.

Because leptospirosis is a range of bacterins, vaccines cannot confer permanent immunity, and so some vets urge you to vaccinate against this annually. In America, however, independent experts, such as Dr Ronald Schultz, head of pathobiology at Wisconsin University, advise that this vaccine should not be used, since it is widely ineffective and is known to cause serious adverse reactions.

All of the warnings and contraindications apply – so you're getting a potentially ineffective vaccine and running the risks of a life-threatening vaccine reaction at the same time.

Feline Infectious Diseases

Cats are routinely vaccinated against:

Cat flu –
Feline herpesvirus and feline callcivirus

This is a rare but potentially life threatening disease whose symptoms include raised temperature, sneezing, watery eyes and nose, and conjunctivitis.

The Veterinary Products Committee (a part of the Department for Food, the Environment and Rural Affairs) states that the cat flu vaccine is not totally protective. According to The Cat Group, supported by the British Small Animal Veterinary Association, the Feline Advisory Bureau, and others, vaccinated cats can become carriers of the viruses and pass them on to others. Let's be clear about this: if you vaccinate your cat against cat flu, you are putting other cats in danger of contracting the disease. The vaccine is keeping the disease in the ecosystem.

As with human flu, cat flu is particularly of concern for the very young and very old, and those who are already unwell or malnourished. Cat flu is spread through close contact with other cats, so indoor cats are not at great risk.

Fort Dodge manufactures a three-in-one cat flu vaccine, containing callcivirus, herpesvirus and panleukopenia virus. Annual vaccination is recommended. Their contraindications warn: 'Pregnant animals should not be vaccinated. Only healthy cats should be vaccinated.

'In the event of an allergic or anaphylactic* reaction, immediate treatment should be given . . . In any population some animals may not respond to vaccination. Successful vaccination depends upon correct storage and administration of the vaccine and the animal's ability to respond. Their ability to respond may be influenced by hereditary factors, concurrent infection, age, nutritional status, some drugs, stress', etc.

* Anaphylaxis is described as a Type I hypersensitivity in which damaging changes are induced by the release of histamine. Anaphylactic shock is an extreme allergic reaction which can lead to

bronchial constriction, dilation of the veins, circulatory collapse, and possible death.

Infectious enteritis
(panleukopenia, feline parvovirus in the UK, or cat distemper in America)

This is a disease that generally affects kittens, and it is usually fatal. Symptoms include sickness and dehydration, and death may be sudden. Adult cats tend to develop natural immunity with age.
Vaccine data sheet contraindications and warnings shown above (please see the Canine Distemper section above) also apply here.

Feline leukaemia virus

This disease can manifest as immune deficiency, anaemia and cancerous tumours or leukaemia. It is generally fatal, although it has been known to be treated with high doses of vitamin C (see http://www.belfield.com).
Again, the leukaemia vaccine is not thought to be 100% effective. Like cat flu, the leukaemia virus is spread through direct contact with other cats, so indoor cats are not at great risk. The Cat Group data sheet says that vaccination will not protect all cats from this disease.
Pfizer's data sheet warns that only healthy cats should be vaccinated. Annual boosters are recommended. Under contraindications, Pfizer warns: 'Post vaccination reactions may occur: pain on injection (generally slight), transient depression, pyrexia (fever), and anorexia. Gastro-intestinal tract disturbance may also occur.
'If an anaphylactic reaction occurs following vaccination, institute treatment immediately ...'. Also don't use immunosuppressant drugs (like steroids) within one month of administration.
The data sheet contraindications and warnings listed under canine distemper also apply here.

Feline chlamydophilosis
(chlamydophilia felis, feline chlamyophilia)

Chlamydophila was formerly known as feline Chlamydia. This is a bacterin which causes conjunctivitis in cats. It is transmitted by direct contact between cats. The vaccine, according to The Cat Group, does not necessarily prevent infection. This disease is not a risk to indoor cats.

Fort Dodge offers a four-in-one vaccine which covers this bacterin. Annual vaccination is recommended. Their contraindications warn: 'Pregnant animals should not be vaccinated. Only healthy cats should be vaccinated.

'In the event of an allergic or anaphylactic reaction, immediate treatment should be given . . .' The company also advised that in any population some animals may not respond to vaccination. Successful vaccination depends upon correct storage and administration of the vaccine and the animal's ability to respond. Their ability to respond may be influenced by 'hereditary factors, concurrent infection, age, nutritional status, some drugs, stress', etc.

Anaphylaxis (potential death) is given as a warning in Fort Dodge's data sheet for this combined vaccine. It seems a high price to pay to avoid conjunctivitis.

Vaccine-Site Cancers in Cats

The American Veterinary Medical Association Vaccine-Associated Feline Sarcoma Task Force initiated several studies, beginning in the late 1990's, to look at the problem of cancers growing in cats at their vaccine injection sites. Dr Dennis W Macey, speaking in DVM magazine, estimated in the 1980s that there were 160,000 vaccine-site tumours in cats each year in America. The problem is so widespread that vets in America have been vaccinating cats in the leg and the tail so that they can amputate when cancer appears. The AVMA Taskforce felt, however, that vaccine-site sarcomas in cats were rare, but described their studies thus:

Selective inhibition of platelet-derived growth factor receptor (PDGFR) activity, 2-year study.

Research conducted in the investigators' laboratory has shown that vaccine-associated feline sarcomas express high levels of a growth factor receptor for platelet-derived growth factor (PDGF). The investigators have found that this growth factor stimulates cells to grow in tissue culture, indicating that it may be one of the dominant factors associated with this cancer. They plan to test a drug to inhibit activity of the PDGF receptor and determine if blocking the receptor inhibits tumour growth. In addition, they will express a mutant receptor in feline cancer cells and determine if this will help inhibit activation of the normal PDGF receptor. The results of this study will help determine if the PDGF receptor contributes to the growth and progression of this aggressive cancer.

Defining the role of the oxidative DNA lesion, 8-hydroxyguanine, in vaccine-associated feline sarcoma.

A basic principle of cancer is that it cannot occur without some interaction with the genetic material of the body DNA. The purpose of this project is to uncover the initial step in the causation of aggressive soft tissue cancers in cats that may be associated with routine administration of vaccines. Since vaccines often cause an inflammatory reaction at the site of injection, highly reactive oxygen-derived free radicals are generated locally that may in some way alter the DNA of certain cells. The investigators will vaccinate a group of cats with commercially available vaccines at three different sites, then determine the concentration of a DNA alteration known as 8-hydroxyguanine that develops at these sites. They will also study this alteration in client-owned cats that develop inflammatory reactions approximately 3 weeks after vaccination. It is hoped that this work will lead to the development of a test to help determine which vaccine components may be causing vaccine-associated sarcomas. Re-formulation of vaccines may then prevent development of these cancers.

Evaluation of mutagenicity of feline vaccines using A_L assay: Year 3.

Little is known about the etiopathogenesis of vaccine-associated sarcomas, but the probability of tumour development seems higher when adjuvanted vaccines have been administered. The investigators hypothesize that adjuvanted vaccines currently in use are inherently mutagenic to mammalian cells as a result of oxidative damage to DNA. In the first year of their research, the investigators used an *in vitro* assay, called the A_L assay, to evaluate the toxicity and mutagenicity of some commonly used feline vaccines. Because adjuvanted vaccines were found to be more toxic and mutagenic than non-adjuvanted vaccines, the researchers continued this line of investigation into a second and third year. They also hypothesize that cats that develop vaccine-associated sarcomas are more susceptible to oxidative damage than are other cats. This hypothesis will be investigated by comparing the anti-oxidant capacity of affected cats with that of unaffected cats.

Molecular biomarkers of vaccine-associated feline sarcoma: alterations in gene expression during tumour development.

The investigators are studying key molecular changes that occur during the development of vaccine-associated feline sarcomas, with the ultimate goal of improving strategies for disease prevention and management. Initial results indicate that there may be a heritable genetic component that makes some cats more prone to tumour development. In the next phase of study, the researchers analyzed specific breeds of cats in the US that may have this predisposition. The results of this investigation will hopefully enable informed decisions to be made regarding the breeding and care of cats with the susceptibility to developing vaccine-associated sarcomas. In this study, the researchers will investigate the entire set of genes that are differentially expressed during tumour development. A comprehensive understanding of these molecular changes will enhance the ability to prevent and treat the disease.

Several facts can be deduced from the above Task Force research:

1. Cats can develop vaccine-site cancers (as can dogs).

2. PDGF (Platelet Derived Growth Factors) are present in the early phases of wound healing and are implicated in tissue fibrosis. Fibrosis (thickening and scarring of connective tissue) is most often a response to inflammation or injury. PDGF is now known to be produced by a number of cell types besides platelets and it has been found to be a mitogen (causes cells to divide) for blood, muscle, bone/cartilage, and connective tissue cells. Vaccines are therefore seen to over-stimulate this biochemical, leading to the uncontrolled division of cells (cancer).

3. Cat vaccines are seen to alter DNA in cats.

4. Vaccine adjuvants are thought to increase the risk of cancer. Adjuvants are chemical substances designed to enhance the immune response to the vaccine. The chemical nature of adjuvants, their mode of action and their reactions (side effects) are highly variable. According to Gupta et al. (1993), some of the side effects can be ascribed to an unintentional stimulation of different mechanisms of the immune system, whereas others may reflect general adverse pharmacological reactions which are more or less expected.

   There are several types of adjuvants, including aluminium hydroxide, aluminium phosphate and calcium phosphate, oil emulsions, products from bacteria, endotoxins (toxic substances released by bacteria), cholesterol, fatty acids, paraffin and vegetable oils.

   Adjuvants are a diverse range of substances which share their ability to enhance the immune response. They are highly variable in terms of how they affect the immune system and how serious their adverse effects are. The use of adjuvants enables the use of less antigen to achieve the desired immune response, and this reduces vaccine production costs. With a few exceptions, adjuvants are foreign to the body and cause adverse reactions.

5. Some cats are more susceptible to vaccine-site cancers than others, and it is not yet known why.

6. Vaccine reactions in cats have stimulated more research funding, to find out which breeds of cat are more likely to develop vaccine-induced cancer. Meanwhile, vaccination continues without that knowledge.

7. Scientists think you should continue to vaccinate your cats, even though they don't know which of your cats are going to get cancer as a result, and they don't know which component of the vaccine will give your cat cancer.

Equine Infectious Diseases

Horses are routinely vaccinated against:

Tetanus

Tetanus is an acute infectious disease affecting all domesticated species and humans, caused by a bacterium. It has a high mortality rate; alternatively, looking at other sources, it is easy to treat. Initial signs are stiffness and unsteady gait, and bloating in ruminants. The disease progresses to the muscles of the jaw and the animals are unable to eat. Mild cases may recover if well nursed. Death is caused by convulsions and respiratory failure. Infection is usually via deep wounds that become contaminated with soil containing the spores.

The Hoechst Roussel product data sheet states that horses should be boosted at intervals of 18-30 months. Contraindications and warnings state: 'In any group of animals, a small number of individuals may fail to respond to vaccination as a result of immunological incompetence or for some other reason. Satisfactory immune responses will only be attained in healthy animals, thus it is important to avoid vaccination of animals which have intercurrent disease or which have a poor nutritional status. As with all vaccines, occasional hypersensitivity reactions may occur.'

See the discussion on hypersensitivity reactions carried in the canine distemper section at the beginning of this chapter.

Equine Herpesvirus (EHV)

EHV is associated with respiratory disease, abortions, and death of newborn foals. EHV is thought to be most prevalent when large numbers of horses are brought together in stressful situations. The Fort Dodge data sheet stipulates that the vaccine is for healthy, susceptible, immune competent horses and ponies. (This means that unhealthy animals should not be vaccinated, and they should not be vaccinated unless they fall into the risk category., i.e., unless they are likely to be introduced to large numbers of horses, staying in areas where EHV is present, or breeding.) Boosting is recommended every six months.

Fort Dodge states in its contraindications: 'The vaccine is safe for administration to pregnant mares but the handling of mares during pregnancy carries its own inherent risks. . . Only healthy horses and ponies should be vaccinated. . . . After administration of any vaccine, a local and/or systemic (affecting the body as a whole) reaction can occasionally occur. The reaction is usually transient.

'In the event of an allergic or anaphylactic* reaction, immediate treatment should be given with a soluble glucocorticoid intravenously, adrenaline intramuscularly or antihistamine intramuscularly. Animals that have received immunosuppressant drugs (e.g., glucocorticoids) should not be vaccinated until at least four weeks have elapsed.'

* Anaphylaxis is described as a Type I hypersensitivity in which damaging changes are induced by the release of histamine. Anaphylactic shock is an extreme allergic reaction which can lead to bronchial constriction, dilation of the veins, circulatory collapse, and possible death.

Equine Influenza

EI is characterised by fever, cough and loss of appetite, and is caused by a flu virus of which there are two types and many strains. Recovery may be complete in a week but secondary bacterial infection can prolong the course of the disease. The horse must be completely rested to avoid lung damage. Vaccination may not be totally effective due to the development of new strains. Annual boosters are recommended.

The Fort Dodge data sheet states in its contraindications: 'The use of these vaccines may cause occasional adverse reactions and, prior

76

to administration, veterinary surgeons are advised to warn clients of the possibility of a local and or systemic reaction.

'Local reactions, more rarely, may be characterised by a marked swelling and very occasionally abscessation. . . . Only healthy horses should be vaccinated. . . . In the event of an allergic or anaphylactic reaction, immediate treatment should be given . . .'

Under 'further information', Fort Dodge adds: 'In any animal population there will be a small number of individuals which fail to respond fully to vaccination. Successful vaccination depends upon correct storage and administration of the vaccine and the animal's ability to respond. Immune competence can be influenced by genetic factors, intercurrent infection, age, nutritional status, drug therapy, stress., etc.'

Strangles (Streptococcus equi)

A contagious disease of horses characterised by fever, respiratory signs, and abscess formations in the lymph nodes of the head. It is caused by a bacterin. Young horses are particularly susceptible. An initial high fever is followed by nasal discharge and swelling of the throat which may obstruct breathing. Lymph nodes may rupture below the jaw, discharging pus. Abscesses may form in other internal organs such as the kidneys, lungs, spleen and liver. Simple cases respond to penicillin.

According to Australian vaccine specialist CSL, '25% of horses infected with strangles do not appear to develop immunity. This makes it very difficult for a vaccine to provide complete protection and it is not claimed that the vaccine is an absolute preventative. However, field experience has shown that vaccination can control the disease by reducing the degree of clinical disease and reducing the number of horses affected.'

According to Elizabeth Anderson, writing in PageWise (http://wy.essortment.com/equinestrangles_rmlh.htm), 'Once Strangles has been confirmed, treatment is relatively simple. In most cases the main form of treatment is to simply monitor the horse's vital signs including temperature, heart rate, and respiratory rate. The disease is self-limiting, and can generally be fought off by the immune system of most healthy horses without outside aid. The use of antibiotics is generally not recommended. By the time the disease manifests its self, antibiotics will no longer be effective at eradicating the infection. In addition, many veterinarians feel that antibiotics will do more harm than good by killing off beneficial bacteria the horse needs to fight the Strangles infection. The most important treatment is simply making the horse as comfortable as possible, encouraging it to eat and drink, and keeping a very close eye out for any possible secondary complications. It may also become necessary to lance and drain extremely infected and swollen exterior lymph nodes.'

Nancy S Loving DVM, writing in myhorsematters.com states, 'Previously, all vaccination strategies against strangles have relied on intramuscular injections that elicit a systemic immune response. These vaccines have had limited efficacy, only curtailing disease in 60-70 percent of those cases challenged by the organism. In addition, many times the intramuscular injections are accompanied by sore muscles, malaise, and a fever. These secondary vaccine reactions may last for as long as a week. Although these complications occur in a small percentage of horses, many horse owners are concerned by these adverse reactions. Having weighed the risks, many have considered that the intramuscular vaccine is seemingly as bad as the horse contracting the disease. For that reason, use of the strangles vaccine has been limited by horse owners until the advent of the intranasal form.'

Vaccine reactions to intramuscular strangles vaccines include injection site swelling and abscess formation. In 'rare cases', a serious vascular inflammation called purpura haemmorrhagica can develop days or weeks after vaccination, which is potentially life-threatening.

An intra-nasal vaccine is available but is not recommended in foals below the age of four months.

West Nile Virus

West Nile Virus affects a horse's neurological system. The virus was found in 1999, and is considered by some, in countries where it is present, to be an epidemic. Transmission of the virus is by mosquitoes. Birds, horses, cats, squirrels, chipmunks, rabbits, and people serve as hosts after being bitten by an infected mosquito. All of these are considered dead-end hosts because they cannot pass the virus to others.

Controlling the mosquito population is said to be the best line of defence. Additional preventive measures for protecting horses should include stabling horses from dusk to dawn, eliminating mosquito breeding areas by filling in low areas, emptying buckets and birdbaths frequently, and cleaning roof gutters.

In 2002, a West Nile vaccine manufactured by Fort Dodge was approved and distributed. Nearly seven million doses were given to horses the first year. In most cases the vaccine was said to have prevented or minimised symptoms and saved the lives of many horses. Although there is a record of horses getting West Nile Virus after one, two, or even three vaccines, the disease is said to be usually milder in those cases. As in most viral diseases, the very young, very old and stressed or immune compromised horses are at most risk.

Stillborn, aborted, and deformed foals may be linked to West Nile Virus vaccine. Reports came in across America of troubled births, including a foal born with no front legs. The foal's mother received her first injection for WNV 30 days into her pregnancy and again two weeks later.

According to the U.S. Department of Agriculture (USDA), there have been several dozen cases of deformities and stillborn foals throughout America, leading to a USDA investigation. The Food and Drug Administration allowed horse owners and veterinarians to begin using the equine vaccine months before its safety and effectiveness had been fully tested.

Although there is a vaccine for horses for use two or three times a year, there is none for humans. According to Carol Glaser, a viral disease expert at the California Department of Health Services, 'Human products have to go through so much scrutiny'. A human vaccine wasn't thought to be potentially available for several years, since safety requirements in human vaccines are far more stringent.

A 1995 issue of the Modern Phytotherapist reported that: 'St John's Wort (Hypericum perforatum) has been proposed as an antiviral agent against enveloped viruses. It has been suggested that preparations standardized to a high level of total hypericin are necessary for significant antiviral activity.'

Dr. Martens from South Dakota has treated horses with full blown reactions to the West Nile Virus with St John's Wort, and they made complete recoveries.

Of large animal vaccines, Christine Chambreau DVM says, 'A veterinarian in Texas stopped vaccinating her horses and the incidence of colic decreased by 95%, a chronic foundering horse became asymptomatic and all 17 horses were healthier in many ways. When she vaccinated the herd five years later because of a panic over one disease, the colics, flu's, and even founder symptoms recurred. A veterinarian in Saskatchewan stopped vaccinating his large beef herd 14 years ago and within two years there was a 75% decrease in his herd mortality.'

Medical editor Matthew Mackay-Smith answered a reader's questions about vaccinating her immune-sensitive horse (EQUUS).

Question: I have owned my 12-year-old light-breed gelding for seven years now in Athens, Greece. He is a bit allergic, with a runny nose and a periodic cough. He also has chronically swollen glands under his jaw and had an episode of hives last spring. For the last two years, after receiving his spring viral vaccinations, he has had three or four rough days. He had colic and was coughing each time. The symptoms passed, but I wonder if this was an allergic reaction to the vaccines and if I should vaccinate him against any viruses. Are any viruses lethal?

Answer: The humid, warm climate of Athens, combined with air pollution, are stressors for equine lungs, and many horses exposed to these conditions exhibit the recurrent airway irritation you describe. Some also develop other signs of immune challenge, such as hives and swollen glands. Your horse does sound like an immune-sensitive individual.

Some viruses, such as rabies, African horse sickness and West Nile virus, can be lethal, but most of the viruses we traditionally vaccinate against, such as influenza and herpesvirus, cause only temporary illness. It may be impossible to determine if your horse's troubles were an allergic response to the vaccine, but it is apparent that your horse is hypersensitive to many things. You may want to try a different brand of vaccine and/or combination of agents.

If your horse's reaction to the vaccine worsens each year, you can be even more sure that it is an allergic response. Whether or not to immunize against a particular disease agent is a decision best made by a local professional who knows the regional risks of disease. Ask your veterinarian if your horse will be more at risk from the immunization shots than from a chance encounter with a random virus.

Matthew Mackay-Smith's answer, although balanced, ignores the licensing requirements stipulated on vaccine data sheets. That is,

80

'vaccines are licensed for use in healthy animals only'. It also supports the belief that vaccines offer a better risk than going without vaccines. It is up to all of us now to examine our belief systems, and to look at alternatives that may be available to us.

It occurred to me to ask the following question: can you think of any other thing human beings do that we know might cause death, in the hope that we will prevent something that we don't know will happen?

Five
Duration of Immunity

Dog and cat owners have been told for many years that it is necessary to vaccinate their dogs and cats every year. 'Responsible' dog and cat owners therefore take their pets for their annual boosters. In the horse world, should a rider wish to compete, they are often forced to vaccinate their animals every six months. In the small animal world, there have been some developments which call annual vaccination into question, and horse owners are also asking their own questions.

What if – like childhood vaccines – pet vaccines give protection for years or life? What if you're spending your money unnecessarily and, worse, what if you're actually making your friends sick, rather than protecting them?

Back in the early 1990s, on the vaccine damage trail, I discovered that there is, actually, no need to vaccinate our pets every year. Worse, vaccines are indeed causing serious debilitating diseases in our pets and, in many cases, vaccines are actually killing them.

I was of course called irresponsible and contentious for saying these things. I was, though, quoting an eminent scientist by the name of Ronald D Schultz who, back in the early 90s, said that:

"Once an animal is immune to viral disease, he is immune for years or life."

The scientific community didn't take much notice of Dr Schultz who, incidentally, is head of pathobiology at Wisconsin University. But in 2003, something important happened. The veterinary profession in America made a public announcement to say that annual vaccination was neither necessary nor without harm. The American Veterinary Medical Association Council on Biologic and Therapeutic Agents (COBTA) presented their consensus, stating:

- When an annual booster vaccination with a modified live virus (MLV) vaccine (i.e., distemper, parvovirus or feline distemper) is given to a previously vaccinated adult animal, no added protection is provided.

82

- MLV vaccines depend on the replication of the virus for a response. Antibodies from previous vaccines do not allow the new virus to replicate.
- Antibody titres are not boosted significantly, memory cell populations are not expanded. No added protection is provided.
- There is no scientific data to support label directions for re-administration of MLV vaccines annually.
- Vaccines are not harmless.
- Unnecessary side effects and adverse events can be minimised by avoiding unnecessary vaccinations.

Translation:

In common everyday language, there is no point vaccinating your dog or cat every year, because there is no benefit. Further, over-vaccination can cause harm to your pets.

Studies have shown that live virus vaccines have been shown to be protective for at least seven years by challenge (where laboratory animals are deliberately subjected to the disease threat), and between 15 and 7 years respectively by blood testing.

Further, COBTA stated that MLV vaccines for viral diseases like parvovirus and distemper provide lifetime immunity when given to adult (over six months of age) dogs and cats

This means that if you decide to vaccinate, you don't need to repeat vaccines for viral disease providing the animal has been vaccinated when he is older than six months of age.

There is, in fact, no scientific evidence to support manufacturers' label directions for annual revaccination. You just don't need to do it – and this is not just my opinion, it is also the view of 'properly quailfied' veterinary specialists. Unfortunately, the veterinary profession seems not to be listening to them.

The problem is that when most animal guardians consult their vets, they will be told to give their animals unnecessary and potentially harmful vaccines year after year until they potentially drop.

The underlying problem, I believe, lies with our governments: licensing authorities are so closely allied to the big businesses they are supposed to be protecting us against, that they have only asked vaccine manufacturers to show that vaccines protect for one year. There has been no requirement for vaccine companies to establish whether or not vaccines provide long-term benefit.

Thankfully, independent scientists have done it for them, and made public announcements to urge against annual shots. I have to bow with respect to the American Veterinary Medical Association. By making this pronouncement, they were potentially reducing the income of themselves and their colleagues by a significant amount. All honour and respect to them.

In response, the British Small Animal Veterinary Association, on its website in 2004, offered vets the following advice (I am happy to share the other view):

'The single most significant contribution has been the report of the UK Veterinary Products Committee (VPC), published in full in 2002 and summarised in the Veterinary Record (2002).

'This report again emphasises the safety and value of vaccination, and presents UK data on the very low prevalence of adverse reactions to these products in dogs and cats. On the issue of extended booster intervals, the VPC recommends that, until such time as more extensive scientific evidence is presented, there is insufficient basis to alter the current data sheet recommendations for companion animal vaccines.'

The BSAVA does suggest, however, that owners might request veterinary surgeons to use revaccination intervals different from those recommended by the manufacturer following an informed discussion of the relative risks and benefits. It's worth emphasising here that the BSAVA encourages dialogue between vets and clients, so that clients can make informed decisions about vaccine regimes. Here's hoping that your vet is open to information that comes from outside the vaccine industry, and doesn't rely solely on the information endorsed by their various professional associations.

Despite the duration of immunity studies and pronouncements made in America, British vets are advised to continue with current vaccine regimes – that is, yearly boosters. This would be unless, of course, they take advantage of some of the new vaccines which have now been licensed for three years, although my friends working in veterinary surgeries tell me, on the whole, that the three-yearly vaccines are not being used.

What the BSAVA doesn't acknowledge, however, and what I have a problem with, is the fact that the advisors to the government on the VPC committee looking into canine and feline vaccines – quoted by the BSAVA - were not, in my view, independent. Two of the four committee members were consultants to a vaccine manufacturer, and one was a member of the Veterinary Defence Society Limited. This means to me that their belief systems, in addition to their financial interests, cannot make them impartial, no matter how hard they try, and no matter how great their integrity. They might be the most noble people on the planet, but as citizens within this democracy, we have to ask the questions. If the individuals looking into canine and feline vaccines were truly free of commercial ties to the vaccine industry, no-one would need to ask this thorny question.

Why is it, if the vaccine industry is so confident of its products, or the government is so confident of vaccine safety, that they don't engage the services of people who are qualified to conduct research, but whose income does not rely upon vaccination or vaccine manufacturers?

Neither does the BSAVA acknowledge the concerns of Canine Health Concern, and others, that the VPC adverse event reporting scheme doesn't work – that we simply don't have an accurate record of adverse events following vaccination: the scheme is voluntary, and vets haven't been educated to recognise adverse vaccine events. Even in the human field, there are grave doubts about the adverse event reporting system. One survey found that only 16% of doctors had ever submitted an adverse event report, and another found that 80% of the reports were filed by only 7% of doctors.

In a letter from Freda Scott-Park, then senior vice president of the British Small Animal Veterinary Association, I was told that, 'We believe that the animal's veterinary surgeon is the right person to consult if an owner has worries about any aspects of the pet's well being and pertinent to this discussion, in relation to the animal's vaccination schedule'.

I'm sorry for being cruel, but I have to highlight the loophole in this view. A news item in the *Wirral Champion* magazine dated January/February 2005, contained the following advice, no doubt from the Forrest Gump School of Veterinary Science:

'Pet owners are often put off vaccination by media scares because they don't know where to ask (for) professional advice – and that is where the Vet on the web can help. Owners can also be confused as to why annual re-vaccination is necessary. The answer is that pets age roughly seven times faster than humans – so medical changes progress that much faster in pets than humans. Where we might need a tetanus vaccine every five years, the cat needs an annual booster.'

You know, if you are an accountant, you have to pass an exam each year to ensure that you keep up-to-date with current financial matters. Money is important, and the professional body associated with money acknowledges this. In the veterinary field, however, it takes the clients and a small selection of vets to stick their heads above the parapet and make the science known, and to get the profession to adhere to current knowledge.

Dr Bob Rogers runs the Critterfixer Animal Hospital in Texas. In 2002, Dr Rogers – who is not a homoeopath – became frustrated with the frequency with which vaccines are repeated in the animal population. He challenged his veterinary colleagues by threatening legal action against them. He wrote to the Attorney General, Consumer Protection Division, Austin, Texas, raising many moral, ethical and scientific questions:

April 17, 2002

Dear Sirs,

I hereby file a complaint against all licensed Veterinarians engaged in companion animal practice in the State of Texas for violation of the Rules of Professional Conduct, rule 573.26 which states: Licensed veterinarians shall conduct their practice with honesty, integrity, and fair dealing to clients in time and services rendered, and in the amount charged for services, facilities, appliances and drugs.

I assert that the present practice of marketing of vaccinations for companion animals constitutes fraud by misrepresentation, fraud by silence, theft by deception, and undue influence by all Veterinarians engaged in companion animal practice in this state.

Recommending, administering, and charging for Canine Corona vaccinations for adult dogs is fraud by misrepresentation, fraud by silence, theft by deception, and undue influence given the literature that states:

1. Dogs over eight weeks of age are not susceptible to canine corona virus disease. Disease produced by canine corona virus has never been demonstrated in adult dogs. Dogs over eight weeks of age that are immunized against canine corona virus will not develop symptoms of canine corona virus disease. Addition of an unnecessary antigen to the vaccination protocol will result in a lesser immunity to the important diseases like parvovirus and distemper, and increase the risk of adverse reactions.

2. Immunologists doubt that Canine corona virus vaccine works, as it would require secretory mucosal IgA antibodies to protect against corona virus and a parenteral vaccine does not accomplish this very well. Twenty-two Schools of Veterinary Medicine including Texas A&M University do not recommend canine corona virus vaccine.

3. Gastroenteroligists at Schools of Veterinary Medicine including Dr Michael Willard at Texas A&M University have stated that they have only seen one case of corona virus disease in a dog in ten years. On several occasions large numbers of dogs have died from adverse reactions to corona virus vaccine.

A reasonable client would not elect corona virus vaccination for an adult dog if presented this information.

Recommending, administering, and charging for re-administration of modified live vaccines like Canine Distemper, Canine Parvovirus, Feline Panleukopenia, injectable Feline Rhinotracheitis, and injectable Feline Calicivirus on an semi-annual, annual, bi-annual or tri-annual basis is theft by deception, fraud by misrepresentation, misrepresentation by silence, and undue influence given the literature that states:

1. The USDA Center for Biologic and Therapeutic Agents asserts that there is no scientific data to support label claims for annual re-administration of modified live vaccines, and label claims must be backed by scientific data.

2. It is the consensus of immunologist that a modified live virus vaccine must replicate in order to stimulate the immune system, and antibodies from a previous vaccination will block the replication of the new vaccinate virus. The immune status of the patient is not enhanced in any way. There is no benefit to the patient. The client is paying for something with insignificant or no effect, except that the patient is being exposed to unnecessary risk of an adverse reaction.

3. A temporal association has been demonstrated between vaccinations and the development of Immune Mediated Haemolytic Anaemia.

4. It has been demonstrated that the duration of immunity for Canine Distemper virus is 7 years by challenge, and 15 years by serology; for Canine Parvovirus is 7 years by challenge, for Feline Panleukopenia, Rhinotracheitis, and Feline Calicivirus is 7.5 years by challenge.

A reasonable client would not elect re-administration of any of the above stated vaccinations for a previously immunized pet if provided with the above information.

The recommendation for administration of Leptospirosis vaccination in Texas is theft by deception, fraud by misrepresentation, misrepresentation by silence and undue influence given the fact that:

1. Although Leptospirosis is re-emerging as an endemic disease for dogs in some areas of the country, Leptospirosis in dogs in Texas is a very rare disease. According to the Texas Veterinary Medical Diagnostic Lab there are only an average of twelve cases of Leptospirosis documented in dogs in Texas per year. Factors to identify those dogs that are at risk have not been identified. Given that there are over 6 million dogs in Texas, the risk of leptospirosis disease to a dog is less than 2 in a million.

2. The commonly used vaccine only contains serovars Lepto. canicola, and Lepto icterohaemorrhagiae, and no cross protection is provided against the other three serovars diagnosed in Texas. Newer vaccines containing Lepto pomona, and Lepto grippotyphosa are available but the duration of immunity is less than one year. To provide protection for a dog against Leptospirosis would require two vaccines with four serovars twice per year.

88

3. Although humans can develop Leptospirosis, the spread of Lepto. from a dog to a human has never been documented and is thought to be a very low risk.

Given the risk of an adverse reaction, a reasonable client would not elect vaccination of their pet if provided with the above information.

The recommendation of Lyme disease vaccine for dogs residing in Texas is fraud by misrepresentation, misrepresentation by silence and undue influence given the literature that states:

1. The Texas Department of Health only reports an average of 70 cases of Human Lyme disease per year in Texas, all of which were likely acquired when people were travelling out of the state.

2. Julie Rawlings reported in her research on the incidence of the Lyme disease organism in ticks in Texas State Parks for the Texas Department of Health that the Borrelia burgdorferi organism is not present in sufficient numbers or in the suitable tick vector for dogs for Lyme disease to be endemic in Texas.

3. Eighty per cent of Lyme disease cases in the U.S. are found in the nine New England States and Wisconsin.

4. Texas A&M College of Veterinary Medicine has not documented one case of Lyme disease in a dog acquired in Texas. Testing on shelter dogs has not revealed a single case.

5. Dr Jacobson, Cornell University has documented a temporal relationship in over 327 cases of dogs, which acquired polyarthritis after the Lyme disease vaccine.

A reasonable client would not elect Lyme disease vaccine for their pet if given this information on the risks vs the benefit.

The recommendation for vaccination of cats with an adjuvanted vaccine without offering a safer alternative vaccine is fraud by misrepresentation, misrepresentation by silence, and undue influence given the literature that states:

1.   Adjuvanted vaccines have been incriminated as a cause of Injection Site Fibrosarcoma in cats.
2.   1:1000 cats vaccinated develop this type of cancer, which is 100% fatal.
3.   Safer alternative non-adjuvanted vaccines are available. A reasonable client would not elect adjuvanted vaccines for their cat if given this information.

The recommendation for vaccination of cats with Feline Infectious Peritonitis vaccine is fraud by misrepresentation, misrepresentation by silence, and undue influence given the literature that states:

1. Feline infectious peritonitis is a rare disease.
2. Eight percent of adult cats carry the normal flora avirulent Feline Corona Virus. On rare occasions this Corona Virus mutates to become a virulent feline Infectious Peritonitis Virus. Every mutation is a different variant and there is no cross protection. This vaccine does not and cannot work.
3. Independent studies have not confirmed the manufacturers claims for efficacy.
4. Twenty-two Schools of Veterinary Medicine and the American Association of Feline Practitioners do not recommend this vaccine.

A reasonable client would not elect this vaccine if given this information.

The recommendation of annual Feline Leukemia Vaccine for adult cats, and cats that are not at risk is theft by deception, fraud by misrepresentation, misrepresentation by silence, and undue influence given the literature that states:

1. Cats over one year of age, if not previously infected, are immune to Feline Leukemia virus infection whether they are vaccinated or not.
2. Adjuvanted Feline leukemia vaccine can cause Injection Site Fibrosarcomas, a fatal type of cancer. This type of cancer is though to occur in 1:10,000 cats vaccinated.

3. Only cats less than one year of age and at risk cats should be vaccinated against Feline Leukemia virus.
A reasonable client would not elect this vaccine for their cat if given this information.

The recommendation of annual rabies vaccination for dogs and cats with three- year duration of immunity vaccine is theft by deception, fraud by misrepresentation, misrepresentation by silence, and undue influence given that:

1. The vaccines has been licensed by the USDA and proven to have duration of immunity of three years by the USDA and seven years by serology by Dr Ron Schultz, therefore annual readministration the client is paying for something with no benefit.

2. Beyond the second vaccination, no data exist to demonstrate that the immune status of the pet is enhanced.

3. The National Association of State Public Health Veterinarians recommendation is for vaccination of dogs and cats for rabies at four months, one year later, and then every three years subsequently. This recommendation has been proven effective in 33 States in the United States.

The recommendation of blood tests for antibody titers on dogs and cats in order to determine if re-administration of vaccine is indicated is fraud by misrepresentation, misrepresentation by silence, and undue influence given the literature that states:

1. The duration of immunity to infectious disease agents is controlled by memory cells, B & T lymphocytes. Once programmed, memory cells persist for life. The presence of memory cells is not taken into effect when testing for antibody titers.

2. Even in the absence of an antibody titer, memory cells are capable of mounting an adequate immune response in an immunized patient. A negative titer does not indicate lack of

immunity, or the ability of a vaccine to significantly enhance the immune status of a patient.

3. A positive titer has not been demonstrated by challenge studies to indicate immunity.
4. The client is paying for a test when a Veterinarian can make no claims about the test results.
5. It has been proven that the re-administration of modified live vaccines has no effect, and that duration of immunity is 7 years or more.

A reasonable client would not elect this test if given this information.

I have brought these deceptive trade practices to the attention of this Board by writing six letters to the board, and appearing before the Board at three Board meetings. The Board members have demonstrated, by the questions that they have asked me, that they are uniformed on these issues, that they have not read the literature that I have sent to support my assertions, and that they have not read the letters I have written. On every occasion the Board members have refused to take any action on these matters.

The Board has also ignored my request to deny approval of Continuing Education credit for seminars on Vaccination of Companion Animals provided by Pfizer Animal Health drug company which are fraudulent by omission of material facts, a conflict of interest, and thereby influence Veterinarians to continue deceptive trade practice in the marketing of vaccines.

The people of the State of Texas have paid over $360 million dollars per year for vaccinations that are unnecessary and potentially harmful to their pets. Over 600,000 pets suffer every year from adverse reactions to unnecessary vaccinations. Many of them die.

A survey by the American Animal Hospital Association shows that less than 7% of Veterinarians have updated their vaccination recommendations, in spite of the fact that these new recommendations have been published twice in every major Veterinary Medical Journal since 1995.

Given that it is the compact of this Board with the State of Texas to protect the people of Texas, and whereby it is provided in the Texas Administrative Code Title 22, Part 24, Chapter 577, Subchapter B, Rule 577.16: Responsibilities of the Board (a) The Texas Board of

Veterinary Medical Examiners is responsible for establishing policies and promulgating rules to establish and maintain a high standard of integrity, skills, and practice in the profession of Veterinary medicine in accordance with the Veterinary Licensing Act, I hereby assert that the Texas State Board of Veterinary Medical Examiners must take demonstrated and thorough action to stop the deceptive trade practices and fraud in the marketing of vaccinations for companion animals.

A reasonable solution would be for the Texas State Board of Veterinary Medical Examiners to request an opinion from the Attorney General on these issues, and for the Texas State Board to issue a policy statement in the Board Notes indicating a Board policy prohibiting each of the practices I have outlined above.

An alternative solution would be to notify every Veterinarian engaged in companion animal practice in this state of the complaint that has been filed against them, and prosecute each and every complaint.

If demonstrated and thorough action to stop the deceptive trade practices has not been taken by this Board within ninety days of receipt of this letter I will file a class action suit against the Texas State Board of Veterinary Medical Examiners on behalf of the people of Texas, for negligence in the execution of their responsibilities, and I will request a Court order to instruct the Board to perform their duties.

Sincerely,

Dr Robert L Rogers

The above statements are true and accurate to the best of my knowledge.

For his troubles on behalf of the animals, Dr Rogers has had fourteen bricks through his window and he has been virtually ostracised by his veterinary peers in Texas. What makes an individual risk this sort of assault? If you look at the science of his statements, it can't just be raw emotion, and his beliefs are certainly more scientific than the vet who believes annual vaccination is required because 'dogs age seven times more quickly than humans'!

In fact, Dr Rogers comes from a long line of people who stood up for the rights of those who needed help, and who were no strangers the wrath of racists and criminals.

Although the senior vice president of the BSAVA feels that a vet is the best person to consult in relation to booster requirements, an

93

awful lot depends upon the knowledge and courage of the vet, doesn't it?

Toni Nyquist is a member of Canine Health Concern's internet discussion group. During February 2005, Toni sent the following post:

'I thought you would all find this rather amusing. I have a foster dog here, an OES Beardie mix. He's going to fly to Rhode Island tomorrow to his new home so I need a Health Certificate. He had shots before he left the shelter last August including a three year rabies vaccine. So the vet is examining him. First he says is he heartworm tested. I said before the shelter. Is he on meds? No - they can do that if they want to on their end. Does he have fleas? No. I use Frontline every THREE years. He says that is impossible. I said check him out. No fleas.

'THEN comes the big one. Vet says he has to have a rabies vaccine within 30 days of the flight. I said that's odd because the airline says as long as he has up to date shots he is okay.
Vet: Well I don't want you to get to the airport and they refuse him.
ME: No, I don't want that either.
Vet: It's only $20.00
ME: That's not the issue. I don't want him over vaccinated.
Vet: Oh it won't hurt him to have extra shots.
ME: OH YES IT CAN AND WILL. UH, HAVE YOU READ THE BOOK, WHAT VETS DON'T TELL YOU ABOUT VACCINES?
Vet walked out.
I called the airline to make sure.
Vet came back by while I was on the phone. The airline coordinator asks me, did the vet tell you he needed another shot? Yes.
She talks to the vet. He handed the phone back to me and told me to go to the reception area.
HMMM - Vet 0 and Over-Vaccination 1. YAY
So Catherine, when the new book comes out shall we send him one? Doubt he'd read it.
Toni

In her letter, Dr Scott-Park also told me that she welcomed the introduction of vaccinations that require boosters at up to three-year intervals. Intervet was the first veterinary vaccine manufacturer to license a three year vaccine. Their press release, dated 1st May 2004, stated:

'The UK will be the first country in the world to offer pet owners a canine vaccine which protects dogs against parvovirus, hepatitis and distemper for three years, thanks to recent developments at Intervet UK.

'Intervet's Nobivac DHPP vaccine will now have a significant impact on vaccination regimes in the UK and help to address dog owners' concerns regarding 'over-vaccination'. The launch follows many years of research and is a significant milestone in vaccine technology. It means that veterinary practices can now offer a vaccination schedule for dogs which minimises the number of components given annually, but still maintains protection for individual pets.

'Intervet has been leading the way for some time in terms of positive changes to canine vaccination regimes in this country having already launched a two-year duration of immunity for these diseases a couple of years ago,' says Jac Bergman, product manager at Intervet UK Ltd. 'With our new extended duration of immunity, owners can benefit from an improved vaccination strategy which means killer diseases like parvovirus, hepatitis and distemper only have to be boosted every three years.'

'The company reiterates, however, the continued importance of visiting the vet every year for an annual health check and the ongoing need to boost dogs against other diseases such as hepatitis.

'Leptospirosis is zoonotic, which means it can easily be transmitted from dogs to humans if the animal is not protected,' continues Jac Bergman. 'The same level of research has also gone into our leptospirosis vaccine and we know scientifically that protection starts to decrease after one year. Therefore annual boosters for this disease are absolutely imperative.'

'Without doubt, vaccination affords vital protection against life-threatening diseases for which there is no cure. Failure to vaccinate means it could only be a matter of time before there are widespread outbreaks of disease in the UK, which have already been seen in other European countries in recent years and have started to appear in pockets throughout the country.

'It is really important that owners continue to see the benefits of vaccination, including annual vaccination against some major diseases,' concludes Jac Berman. 'Moreover, it's important that owners realise the real risks they run if they cease to protect their pets against infectious diseases.'

Although the company now offers a three-year vaccine, in February 2005, Intervet launched its 'vaccine amnesty' campaign with a double page advertisement and an editorial in *Veterinary Review*. The aim was to encourage more pet owners whose animals' booster vaccinations have lapsed to go back to its customers' practices. According to Intervet's news item, 'Research shows that one out of five pets receiving a primary course of vaccinations will not return for their first annual booster. The uptake of subsequent boosters remains even lower, according to the most recent data (October 2004) from the Management Analysis Index.

'Jac Bergman, product manager at Intervet UK says: 'It is imperative that vets raise awareness of the importance of a pet's annual booster.'

To support the amnesty, Intervet developed an information pack, containing a range of promotional and training materials, to assist veterinary practices in raising the profile of their clinic within the community.

Back to our esteemed expert's press release in *Wirral Champion*: '... some vet practices work with vaccine suppliers to offer a Vaccination Amnesty. In simple terms this means that the owner books their pet in for the whole course, but gets it for the cost of the single annual booster. Bargain or what?'

What this means is that some vets believe that if a twelve-monthly booster is missed, then the animal has to receive the whole puppy course all over again, which means two shots around two weeks apart, according to the Wirral vetonetheweb's website. Just to make sure I hadn't misunderstood, I contacted the practice to find out whether the Vaccine Amnesty was offering the lepto shot as an amnesty, or whether they were offering vaccination against viral diseases which actually don't need annual boosting. Yep – they're offering the whole lot – two shots for the price of one.

Personally, I stopped going to the sales many years ago – you always end up buying something you didn't want or need in the first place. However, thanks to Intervet, vets have more choice – they can go with the company's new three-year booster plan, or offer the one-size-fits-all annual package. It's no wonder vets are confused with all the conflicting information. Do they need to vaccinate annually, or every three years? Do they listen to the duration of immunity studies which say vaccines against viral disease are good for years or life? What do they do?

In her letter to me of May 2004, Freda Scott-Park wrote: 'There has been much made of the accusation that we are 'ripping off' clients by vaccinating their pets; my colleagues in practice make the point that they will make more money from treating an animal with parvovirus or distemper than they will from the annual check up and vaccination – however no-one wants to have to treat these quite heart-breaking preventable diseases. As regards the safety of routine vaccination, we now have evidence from the recent 'Practice Overview of Canine Health' (the Animal Health Trust/vaccine industry study) that clearly indicates that there was no temporal association with recent vaccination (within the previous three months) of any increase in signs of ill health.'

Dr Scott-Park also said, 'The main concern is to ensure that all animals are protected against preventable diseases – we accept that studies like the recent paper by Bohm et al in the *Veterinary Record* (April 10, 2004) add greatly to our knowledge of protective antibody titres in unvaccinated animals. But it indicates also that some dogs remain susceptible to disease and emphasizes that an annual booster for leptospirosis in endemic areas remains essential'.

Please note the Dr Scott-Park did not say that annual vaccination against viral disease is essential, but that annual vaccination against leptospirosis is essential. However, the scientists disagree on the point of leptospirosis – some say it shouldn't be given at all.

Heck, it's no wonder we're all confused. Perhaps, though, this is just a reflection of the times we are living through. Maybe we are all struggling for clarity.

Two people in America have taken the bull by the horns and approached the legislature in order to a) stop unnecessary rabies vaccination, which harmed their dog, and b) get vets to disclose the possible adverse reactions animals can have to vaccines. In February 2005, Peter and Kris Christine testified to the Agriculture, Conservation and Forest Committee in Maine. Kris's testimony follows:

My name is Kris Christine and I live with my family in Alna, Maine. Before I begin my testimony, I'd like to advise the committee that one of the world's leading veterinary research scientists, Dr. W.

97

Jean Dodds, wanted to be here today to testify in support of LD429, but could not do so because of prior commitments. With her permission, in the attachments to my testimony, I have included her letter to Representative Peter Rines dated February 17, 2005 (Attachment 5) resolutely endorsing this first-in-the-nation veterinary vaccine disclosure legislation.

I am here today to respectfully urge this committee to recommend passage of LD429 - An Act to Require Veterinarians to Provide Vaccine Disclosure Forms because pet owners need the scientifically proven durations of immunity (how long vaccines are effective for) in order to make informed medical choices for their animals.

Many Maine veterinarians have failed to inform clients that most core veterinary vaccines protect for seven or more years, and pet owners, unaware that their animals don't need booster vaccinations more often, have unwittingly given their companions useless booster shots - taking an unnecessary toll on their finances and animals' health. The human equivalent would be physicians vaccinating patients against tetanus once every year, two years, or three years and not disclosing that the vaccines are known to be protective for 10 years.

For years veterinarians have sent pet owners annual, biennial and triennial reminders for redundant booster shots and justified it with vaccine manufacturers' labeled recommendations. According to the American Veterinary Medical Association's (AVMA) Principles of Vaccination (Attachment 6), "..revaccination frequency recommend-dations found on many vaccine labels is based on historical precedent, not on scientific data ... [and] does not resolve the question about average or maximum duration of immunity [Page 2] and may fail to adequately inform practitioners about optimal use of the product...[Page 4] ." As the Colorado State University Veterinary Teaching Hospital states it: "...booster vaccine recommendations for vaccines other than rabies virus have been determined *arbitrarily* by manufacturers."

Dr. Ronald Schultz, Chairman of Pathobiological Sciences at the University of Wisconsin School of Veterinary Medicine, is at the forefront of vaccine research and is one of the world's leading authorities on veterinary vaccines. His challenge study results form the scientific base of the American Animal Hospital Association's (AAHA) 2003 Canine Vaccine Guidelines, Recommendations, and Supporting Literature (Attachment 7). These studies are based on science - they are not arbitrary. The public, however, cannot access this data. The American Animal Hospital Association only makes this report available to veterinarians, not private citizens, and Maine's pet owners are unaware that the AAHA Guidelines state on Page 18 that: "We now know that booster injections are of no value in dogs already immune, and immunity from distemper infection and vaccination lasts for a minimum of 7 years based on challenge studies and up to 15 years (a lifetime) based on antibody titer." They further state that hepatitis and parvovirus vaccines have been proven to protect for a minimum of 7 years by challenge and up to 9 and 10 years based on antibody count. So, unless the Legislature passes LD429 requiring veterinarians to provide vaccine disclosure forms, dog owners who receive an annual, biennial, or triennial reminder for booster shots will not know that nationally-accepted scientific studies have demonstrated that animals are protected a minimum of 7 years after vaccination with the distemper, parvovirus, and adenovirus-2 vaccines (see Page 12 AAHA 2003 Guidelines attached, and Table 1, Pages 3 and 4).

"My own pets are vaccinated once or twice as pups and kittens, then never again except for rabies," Wall Street Journal reporter Rhonda L. Rundle quoted Dr. Ronald Schultz in a July 31, 2002 article entitled Annual Pet Vaccinations may be Unnecessary, Fatal (Attachment 2). Dr. Schultz knows something the pet-owning public doesn't - he knows there's no benefit in over-vaccinating animals because immunity is not enhanced, but the risk of harmful adverse reactions is increased. He also knows that most core veterinary vaccines are protective for at least seven years, if not for the lifetime of the animal.

The first entry under Appendix 2 of the AAHA Guidelines (Attachment 7) "Important Vaccination 'Do's and Don'ts" is "Do Not Vaccinate Needlessly - Don't revaccinate more often than is needed and only with the vaccines that prevent diseases for which that animal is at risk." They also caution veterinarians: "Do Not Assume that Vaccines Cannot Harm a Patient - Vaccines are potent medically active agents and have the very real potential of producing adverse events." Very few pet owners have had this disclosed to them.

The AVMA's Principles of Vaccination (Attachment 6) states that "Unnecessary stimulation of the immune system does not result in enhanced disease resistance, and may increase the risk of adverse post-vaccination events." (page 2) They elaborate by reporting that:

"Possible adverse events include failure to immunize, anaphylaxis, immunosuppression, autoimmune disorders, transient infections, and/or long-term infected carrier states. In addition, a causal association in cats between injection sites and the subsequent development of a malignant tumor is the subject of ongoing research." (Page 2)

Referring to adverse reactions from vaccines, the Wall Street Journal article cited above (Attachment 2) reports: "In cats there has been a large increase in hyperthyroidism and cancerous tumors between the shoulder blades where vaccines typically are injected." With modified live virus vaccines (distemper, parvovirus, hepatitis), some animals can actually contract the same disease which they are being inoculated against. If the public knew an animal's immunity to disease is not increased by overvaccination, they would certainly not consent to expose their pets to potential harm by giving them excessive booster shots.

Veterinary vaccines are potent biologic drugs - most having proven durations of immunity much longer than the annual, biennial or triennial booster frequencies recommended by vaccine manufacturers and veterinarians. They also carry the very real risk of serious adverse side affects and should not be administered more often than necessary to maintain immunity.

The extended durations of immunity for vaccines is not "new" or "recent" science as some members of the Maine Veterinary Medical Association (MVMA) have claimed. AAHA reveals on Page 2 of their Guidelines that ideal reduced vaccination protocols were recommended by vaccinology experts beginning in 1978. A Veterinary Practice News article entitled "Managing Vaccine Changes" (Attachment 3) by veterinarian Dennis M. McCurnin, reports that: 'Change has been discussed for the past 15 years and now has started to move across the country'.

According to a September 1, 2004 article in the DVM veterinary news magazine (Attachment 1), the 312 member Maine Veterinary Medical Association (MVMA) "champions full disclosure of vaccine information to pet owners." MVMA president, Dr. Bill Bryant, is quoted as stating: "Its time for something like this to come out … disclosure forms will be an important resource to have available, [and] if it goes before the Legislature, we'd likely support it."

It is time. Pet owners have the right to know the scientifically proven durations of immunity for the veterinary vaccines given their animals, as well as the potential adverse side effects and benefits. LD 429 would make that standardized information available to all pet owners.

Peter Christine testified:

My name is Peter Christine of Alna, Maine and I am here today to voice support for L.D. 429 The information contained in the American Animal Hospital Association's 2003 Canine Vaccine Guidelines, Recommendations, and Supporting Literature is not available to the public. At present, the only information about vaccines, their benefits, risks, and durations of immunity comes from veterinarians who derive income from vaccinations.

This is a clear conflict of interest. That veterinarians are boostering with vaccines on one, two and three year schedules with vaccines that have proven durations of immunity of 7 years or more is evidence that the scientific data of Dr. Ronald Schultz's study contained in the AAHA Guidelines, is being disregarded.

I work in the real estate profession where disclosure to prospective buyers of material facts and defects of a property is not left solely to the discretion of the real estate agent. By law we must provide a document signed by the seller itemizing this information and are under a legal obligation to reveal any material defects "of which the real estate brokerage agency knew or, acting in a reasonable manner, should have known." To do otherwise would be self-serving.

The veterinary profession, likewise, should be required to make available material facts regarding vaccinations. The absence of such information to-date has allowed a continuance of the practice of over-vaccination which provides no additional benefit, incurs needless expense to consumers, and jeopardizes the health of the animal.

A disclosure should and can be manageable. A concise example is the tetanus/diphtheria vaccination disclosure from the Center for Disease Control which was readily available from my physician (and is attached). It is written in layman's terms and provides the necessary information for patients to make educated decisions. A document containing the benefits, risks, and possible side effects of a particular vaccination, and references to the vaccine durations of immunity contained in the AAHA Guidelines, would give consumers the facts required for an informed discussion with their veterinarian about the best vaccination schedule for their animal.

Mention has been made of the cost to the state and to the veterinarians of such legislation. Should the legislation not pass, consideration should be given the needless expense to consumers, as well as the health risks posed to animals by an uninformed acceptance of overly frequent vaccination routines having no basis in proven durations of immunity.

I urge you to vote this legislation 'ought to pass'.

When I started Canine Health Concern back in 1994, I did so because information contained in this book, and in *What Vets Don't Tell You About Vaccines* was not available to the pet owning population. I felt it should be available, and that I could not live in a world where the animals were being harmed through a consensus of silence. When this information is made available by veterinarians, then my job will be done, and I can go and live my life. Thanks to people like Kris and Peter, and others around the world, our unpaid and heartbreaking work may be over. I look forward to that day.

Until that day, animal guardians still face a dilemma. On the one hand they are likely to meet vets in practice who use questionable logic to support annual vaccination, or who have managed to overlook the scientific data. On the other hand, vets themselves appear to be disagreeing about the frequency with which vaccines should be given. In the horse world, duration of immunity studies appear to be in short supply. In cats it is acknowledged that vaccines can cause cancer; in dogs it is acknowledged that vaccines can cause various immune-mediated diseases.

Even knowing this, or maybe *not* knowing this, many vets say you should vaccinate annually. Others – even some homoeopaths – acknowledge that vaccines come with serious risks, but feel that an initial course and a first-year booster should be given. Others, still, are recommending vaccination every three years. Meanwhile, the vaccine manufacturers are doing their job: they are seeking to sell their products.

I hope that I have demonstrated the confusion regarding revaccination, and illustrated why it is so important for animal guardians to be involved in the decision making process.

Six
The Homoeopathic Vaccine Alternative

I wish I could, as I did in *'What Vets'*, give you a suitable alternative to vaccination. But as time has moved on, I find that homoeopaths themselves disagree about the homoeopathic nosode, which some advocate giving instead of vaccines.

The nosode is based upon the homoeopathic principle, although it is not strictly homoeopathy in that it can be given as a preventative as well as to treat disease. The nosode is, essentially, a minute dilution of the disease-causing agent. It can be supplied in pill or liquid form and dropped onto your animal's tongue or placed in their water (there are also nosodes against human viral and bacterial disease). Although the pathogen cannot be measured in its diluted state, nosodes are said to activate the energetic body to recognise a pathogen and fight the challenge. Conventional science has a problem with the whole philosophy of homoeopathy, so most conventional vets will have been trained to believe that homoeopathy can't work. They frequently say that nosodes are unproven. I've even heard homoeopaths saying this.

Some studies do, however, exist.

Christopher Day was invited into a kennel in Oxfordshire, England, where there was a kennel cough outbreak, and he had the wisdom to invite a vaccine manufacturer in at the same time so that a trial could be conducted. There were 40 dogs in the kennel; eight had been vaccinated against kennel cough, 22 had not. Of the vaccinated dogs, all had developed a cough, whereas 19 of the 22 unvaccinated dogs had developed a cough.

A homoeopathic nosode was given to all the dogs who entered the infected boarding premises subsequently: one dose on entry, and twice daily for three days. There were 214 dogs entering the kennel during the rest of the summer, all of whom received the nosode. 64 had been conventionally vaccinated, and 150 had not prior to entry into the kennel.

Of the 214 dogs, three of the 64 vaccinated dogs contracted kennel cough. One of the 150 non-vaccinated dogs contracted kennel cough. As a further exercise, any dogs showing just one very transient sign of kennel cough were recorded. This showed that 51 of the 64 vaccinated dogs showed evidence of slight symptoms, whereas only 40 of the 150 non-vaccinated dogs showed any symptoms. Chris Day felt that this showed that vaccines were harmful in this situation.

Christopher Day reported:

a)   Nosodes can very effectively stop, in its tracks, an outbreak of a highly transmissible disease (viz kennel cough);

b)   That it does so, in this case, more effectively than the currently available vaccines;

c)   That vaccination impairs the ability of the animal to respond to the nosode.

John Saxton MRCVS VetMFHom, in *IJVH* Volume 5, No 1, 1991, presented a paper describing the use of the canine distemper nosode in disease control. Although not presented as a clinical trial, it was presented as a report upon a clinical problem that was significantly relieved by the use of nosodes.

This involved a boarding kennels dealing solely with stray dogs under contract to the local police authority. As such, vaccination status was unknown. All animals not claimed or re-homed were destroyed on the eighth day after arrival.

When the dogs arrived at the kennels, they were screened by experienced staff and those with no obvious signs of disease or injury were admitted directly into the main kennels. All others were placed in an isolation block for examination by veterinary staff.

It became clear that there was an unacceptably high incidence of clinical distemper associated with the kennels, despite all possible screening and management procedures. It was therefore decided to use the canine distemper nosode as a control measure in addition to general management measures. The homoeopathic nosode was prepared from a local clinical case, using nasal and ocular discharge, plus a swab from the tonsils. Prepared as a liquid, the nosode was administered via the dogs' drinking water.

The results showed that, of dogs kept in the kennels for eight days, 11.67% showed clinical signs of distemper on the 5th day prior to the introduction of nosodes, dropping to 4.36% after the nosodes were introduced. When the entire kennel population was taken into account (including those dogs who left prior to the eighth day), the incidence of distemper dropped from 8.05% to 2.81% after the introduction of nosodes.

Interestingly, the incidence of distemper rose markedly in the 8th and 11th months of the trial. Upon investigation, it was realised that one of the kennel staff had left the homoeopathic supply in direct sunlight for several hours prior to administration. When this storage practice was remedied, incidences of distemper dropped once again – indicating that the homoeopathic remedies were, indeed, having a positive effect.

Incidentally, I was fortunate to meet Juliette de Baircli Levi, the wonderful vet who wrote 'The Complete Herbal Handbook for the Dog and Cat'. Juliette told me that she was very successful in curing distemper in dogs by fasting and giving grapefruit juice. She added that the success rate was much higher with non-vaccinated as opposed to vaccinated dogs.

A trial was conducted by W Jonas, A Fortier, D Heckendorn and C Macy during 1991, and a paper was presented at the 5th LIBI meeting in Paris. The paper was entitled *'Prophylaxis of Tularaemia Infection in Mice Using Agitated Ultra High Dilutions of Tularaemia Infected Tissues'*.

Homoeopathic dilutions from reticulo-endothelial tissues of mice infected with Tularaemia were administered orally to a group of mice; a control group was treated with dilutions of ethanol. The mice were then challenged with Tularaemia, and survival time and mortality were evaluated. After 15 experiments, the very high homoeopathic dilutions produced a significant increase in survival time and a significant reduction in total mortality compared to non controls (*Homoeopathy – frontier in medical science*, published by North Atlantic Books).

Another trial was conducted by Susan Wynne and Ronald Schultz to see of the parvovirus nosode could protect puppies against parvo. It showed that nosodes did not protect those puppies, although Drs Wynne and Schultz themselves admit that the trial was flawed.

Richard Pitcairn DVM, author of 'Natural Health for Dogs and Cats' advocates the use of nosodes, as does Martin Goldstein DVM in 'The Nature of Animal Healing'. Hahnemann, the father of homoeopathy, presented many cases of nosodes reducing the incidence of disease contraction, and there have been several studies to show that nosodes are successful in the prevention of childhood diseases.

So there isn't much research available to support the use of nosodes. On the other hand, they have been used on animals in the UK for at least thirty years, with very few incidences where animals given nosodes succumbed to disease. Indeed, there is a huge body of anecdotal evidence to support the use of nosodes in dogs, cats, horses and other domestic animals.

The lack of scientific proof of nosodes stems, it seems, from the fact that no-one has paid for the necessary trials. Anyone can make a nosode if they know how. Containing natural substances, nosodes cannot be patented, so there is little incentive for pharmaceutical companies to test their efficacy.

Nosodes offer a dilemma for homoeopathic vets, however. The veterinary bodies and vaccine manufacturers will lend their full support to a vet when it goes wrong after administration of a vaccine. This support will not be forthcoming if a nosode fails to work. I think, also, that homoeopathic vets tend to be very 'reasonable' and open-minded in their approach – it is this virtue which led them into this discipline in the first place. They are less likely to be rigid in their beliefs (one assumes), and so they are more likely to be 'iffie' about a vaccine alternative that has not had rigorous scientific scrutiny and research material to quote if things go wrong.

One homoeopathic vet told us at a recent CHC Foundation in Canine Healthcare workshop that he saw the nosode fail three dogs in a family three years previously, and so now advocates minimal vaccines instead. This is indeed an option, providing animal guardians are also warned of the potential adverse reactions to vaccines. I would also point out that vaccines have been known to fail on occasion – the manufacturers themselves will admit this. And I'd also ask where the nosodes came from, so that their quality can be verified.

Chris Day, whilst being equally reasonable, will tell you that he has only seen the nosode fail once, and that was with a dog who developed parvo but recovered very quickly (within a couple of days). Chris does not administer vaccines and cautions people to obtain their nosodes from a suitably qualified homoeopathic vet in order to ensure quality.

106

There is a further complication in that some classical homoeo-pathic vets, particularly in America, claim that nosodes can cause unwanted side-effects.

Christine Windham-Thomas, a long-time CHC member and student of homoeopathy, presented the following information as part of her CHC Foundation in Canine Healthcare coursework. She has given her permission for these thoughts to be shared here. Christine writes:

Nosodes have a very special place in homeopathy:

1. As a remedy used during the treatment of disease – i.e. the use of the Parvo Nosode during the treatment of Parvo. Hering noted that he had never succeeded in curing, only ameliorating disease when he used nosodes in this manner. So, nosodes can be used during the treatment of a disease in order to help other more similar remedies to complete the cure.

2. Nosodes are used as inter-current remedies in the treatment of chronic disease. This is the most common use of nosodes in homeopathic practice. When, during the treatment of chronic disease, the similar remedy stops working, the use of the nosode at this point in the healing process will remove the obstacles to cure and allow the similar remedy to continue the cure.

3. As the constitutional remedy during the treatment of chronic disease. In this instance, the nosode will be prescribed on the totality of the patient's symptoms just like any other remedy.

4. Homeopathic Prophylaxis. Hahnemann did the first use of a homeopathic remedy in prophylaxis, when he used the remedy Belladonna as prophylaxis for Scarlatina. Another one of Hahnemann's followers, Boenninghausen, successfully prevented Smallpox with the use of Variolinum - the nosode for Smallpox. His work has been misunderstood and misapplied for many, many years. Boenninghausen's use of Variolinum prevented healthy people from becoming infected with Smallpox during an epidemic. This is how nosodes should be used in a prophylactic/preventive manner.

5. Nosodes have a tendency to produce strong aggravations when misused. This is one reason we see cases of Parvo, (mostly) and Distemper after the use of nosodes that have been used in very high potencies and/or repeated too often.

It is extremely important to remember several things:

♦ Nosodes are used to prevent disease only during an epidemic. So, the use of Parvo or Distemper nosodes should be reserved for those times when there is an epidemic going around, or when the possibility of a young puppy coming in contact with these diseases is high. For example, giving the Parvo nosode in 30c potency (never use the nosodes in a potency higher than 30C) for 2 or 3 days prior to the puppy going to the vet's, or obedience class, where the puppy will come in contact with other vaccinated puppies shedding the viruses from vaccines.

♦ With puppies born to breeders who have not vaccinated for many generations and who feed naturally, the best protection is a healthy immune system.

♦ Nosodes are made with noxious substances. Although the original substance is no longer present in 30c potency, the energy of the disease most certainly is. So, when you give Parvo nosodes to a 3-week-old puppy, you are giving this puppy the energy of Parvo. Not only does this practice not protect during an outbreak, but the puppy can develop symptoms of chronic disease by the time they are 10-12 weeks of age.

♦ Nosodes should never be given after a vaccine to "antidote" the vaccine. This is another misconception of a classical homeopathic practice and should not be done.

♦ Once you have given a young puppy the nosode in order to keep them healthy during an epidemic, it is not necessary to continue to repeat the nosode. Repetition will only enhance the chances of aggravations and/or nosode induced disease.

♦ Nosodes do not confer immunity.

I suspect that you'll find as many different views about nosodes coming from homoeopaths as there are homoeopaths. Annoyingly, it seems to me that the jury is as out on nosodes as it is on vaccines. I would therefore advise anyone considering the use of nosodes, or vaccines, to consult their conventional vet and their homoeopathic vet, gather the experiences of other animal guardians, and study the available literature. I would *not* advise you to act upon anyone else's decision. A homoeopathic vet may advise you to vaccinate, for example. This advice is no doubt given in good faith, to the best of their knowledge – but you are the one who must sit with your loved one if anything should go wrong - not them.

In my experience, if someone tells you what you should do, the person doing the telling is lacking in wisdom. No wise person would seek to disempower you. Never give your power away to anyone.

The following email correspondence took place between myself and Lisa Mayhew during December 1998. I am reproducing it here because I want to speak to the homoeopathic vets who currently doubt the nosode. We know that vaccines do not guarantee protection – vaccine manufacturers themselves tell us this. Neither do nosodes. But if homoeopaths believe in homoeopathy, then perhaps they will think again before running back to vaccines. Nosodes currently give us the only alternative to vaccines. Is death by parvo or distemper any worse than the following scenario?

Please note that I am not shouting at anyone, or telling any homoeopathic vet what they must do. I am just asking that we broaden the picture. If, after doing this, you choose to advocate vaccination, then I respect your right to think and act as you feel compelled to think and act, as I would ask you to respect everyone else's right to do the same.

Dear Catherine

I hope you don't mind my asking your advice, but we're in a quandary as to whether to finish our puppy's course of vaccinations, due to your book!

I should have known better, as I had a lot of problems with my horse and his vaccinations. Anyway, we got the puppy a few weeks ago and he had his first jab at eight weeks old, with no problems. He was meant to have the second last Friday (12 weeks old) but I found your book in the library and we put it off so that I could administer homoeopathic buffer pills in time. Having read more over the weekend, we put it off again this morning in a panic!

What I would really like to find out (if you know) is whether if we have the second jab, does that provide us with a 'legal' vaccine certificate for future use (shows, training, etc.) if we then follow homoeopathic protection instead of annual boosters? Or must the certificate show updates of annual boosters?

We just don't know what to do - we are loath to administer the second jab now, but almost feel that as we've done the first, we might as well do the second. I'd appreciate it if you could advise me in any way, as soon as possible

Lisa Mayhew

Dear Lisa

Many thanks for your e-mail. I have to say, first, that it is not my place to tell you whether or not you should vaccinate your puppy, although my feelings on the subject are probably well known to you by now! When I say it's not my place, I am trying to say that I don't have a right to force an important decision like this on you.

I know that horses can't compete in events unless they have a vaccine certificate to show, but I don't think it's quite so bad in the dog world. Some shows/training classes insist upon up-to-date vaccines, but I don't believe they actually ask the owners to show the certificates. Other dog clubs, kennels, etc., are beginning to accept the homoeopathic nosode as an alternative to vaccines.

We estimate that around three in every hundred dogs is vaccine damaged, which means that you have a 97% chance that your pup will be OK. You really need to assess the risk of your individual case. In the human field, doctors are told (by Merck, a vaccine manufacturer) that 'people' with, or from families prone to, skin disease, inhalant allergies, food allergies, heart disease and neurological conditions should not receive live vaccines, because the vaccines could induce a severe or fatal infection. Do you happen to know whether any of these conditions are prevalent in your pup's line?

My two youngest pups have never been vaccinated. They are both incredibly fit, and we haven't had a day's illness in their 19 months of life. They are given the homoeopathic nosode, and we were recently accepted at a training class, despite the trainer's card saying, 'we accept fully vaccinated dogs for training'. I know lots of people who show their dogs, and have never heard any of them say that they were refused entry because they don't vaccinate.

So good luck with your decision, and big kisses for the pup.

Catherine

Many thanks for your kind and swift reply. I have done a lot of phoning around of kennels, trainers, my breeder, etc., and after much deliberation last night my husband and I decided that although we hated doing it, we would have the second jab and no further boosters (protect him in future homoeopathically). So, I've just come back from the vet, card in hand, hoping nothing goes wrong. Keep your fingers crossed for Zulu (our puppy) please!

I will fill your survey form in after a few months. Thanks very much for all your efforts, and your excellent book.

Lisa Mayhew

I do hope Zulu lives a long, healthy and happy life. You'll find, though, that you'll hit the same problem if you don't have a 'current' vaccine certificate.

Catherine

I am writing to you again as I thought you should know that things have not gone well with Zulu, our puppy. We feel unbelievably horrible about it, more so because we had such strong misgivings about giving the second vaccine, and things could have been different now.

Zulu had his second jab last Tuesday and on Sunday he was very quiet/sleepy (highly unusual). Monday morning he was very unwell - fever and listless, so I took him to our vet who gave him antibiotic capsules. He had a fever of 104.6.

By Monday evening his fever was 105.8 and I was vaguely hysterical, so we took him back to the vet, who gave him a fever-reducing jab. That helped for a few hours only and he ate some chicken. This morning he was even worse and we took him for an early morning vet visit - fever at 104, totally weak, and he got a jab of antibiotics. By this afternoon I could see he was just getting worse, so listless, groaning, twitching, so hot and no strength whatsoever. We have to carry him to wee or he wets himself.

I got hold of a homoeopathic vet in a bit of an emotional state and decided to drive to fetch the remedy. When I got there I saw him and he gave me some other remedies, which we gave Zulu as soon as I got back home. My husband is at the moment sleeping with him in his cage, and he seems quieter and more peaceful - but we don't know if that's good or bad.

The vets have insisted that if it was due to the vaccine, it would have happened within 24 hours of the jab - but don't diseases take at least a few days to develop? One vet even advised us that it could be from other animals, like perhaps birds!!? (Zulu has stayed mostly indoors since Tuesday, and doesn't go far in the garden). We just desperately wish that we'd listened to our inner voices and previous experience.

Lisa

I am so sorry to hear about Zulu, but I'm afraid I'm not surprised. It seems to happen time and time again. As soon as people start asking 'should I, shouldn't I?', and then go ahead and do it from a position of fear, the dog has a reaction. But had I said that to you, then I would have been using undue pressure. I'm very glad that you have a homoeopath on the case.

Our dogs are our teachers. I know it is very hard for you at the moment, and I do hope that Zulu makes a full recovery - but can you imagine how despondent I feel when, even having read my book, people still vaccinate? How, Lisa, can we get through to people so they don't have to watch their dogs suffer first?

As for the vet saying it has to happen within 24 hours - get him to read my book. Serum reactions can happen 10 days after the jab (and vaccines contain serum). MLV vaccines multiply in the animal over time (i.e., the virus multiplies slowly until such time as the animal combats the vaccine challenge, or not). The vet is supposed to be a scientist! They don't seem to understand the fundamentals. Sorry - I am very upset to hear about Zulu.

Catherine

Zulu was put down last night - December 24th - at approximately 10pm, but we knew he gave up really yesterday morning. We're devastated, so I won't say much more.

Lisa

I am so very sorry. I am heartbroken for you. Zulu was a warrior - remember him as such.

Catherine

Dear Catherine

I just felt I wanted to answer a question you posed in one of your e-mail's, regarding how one can get through to people without having to watch their dogs suffer first.

Well, I was very worried before Zulu's second vaccine and began asking advice as I didn't trust my own judgment. I postponed the jab twice and read most of your book, tried to speak to the homoeopathic vet, e-mailed you, spoke to the breeder, spoke to a dog trainer, phoned up kennels.

The homoeopath's secretary basically told me to make up my own mind, and said I could speak to him in a week's time. You mentioned that, "had I said that to you, then I would have been using undue pressure". But then everyone else on the 'other side' applied plenty of pressure - 'just' to have the second one. All I needed was a voice on your side saying no, believe in this, homoeopathy is better. Some reassurance.

I'm not blaming anyone except myself for not being stronger and listening to my inner voice that made me hesitate in the first place. I just thought you might like to know what I tried to do/find out and how perhaps equal pressure needs to be exerted on the anti-vaccine side. If there isn't any it almost seems to indicate a lack of belief in the homoeopathic system, which is what might make people vaccinate after all.

If I can ever help with your work, please let me know. I really appreciated your responses to my questions, it's good to know that people care so much.

Lisa

Dear Lisa

I know exactly what you mean - the pro-vaccinators do apply extreme pressure. I often despair when I hear homoeopaths saying that the nosodes are unproven. Indeed, at a seminar, where a homoeopathic pharmacist was speaking, and saying that nosodes were unproven, I sort of imploded, saying that they are NOT unproven and this is the only alternative we have, so be positive about it! It drives me mad when people, who know the truth, insist upon being 'reasonable', when the other side are being bullies.

However, I honestly do believe that no human being has a right to compel another to do anything - that's where we went wrong in the first place, with the men in white coats. Do we want to replace one set of 'experts' with another set of 'experts' - human beings who are just as open to corruption and self interest as the first set? Despite this, I am known as 'that awful woman' who is obsessed about vaccines - a lot of people out there already think I'm extreme.

I felt that I had put enough information in my book to help you make your decision. After reading the book, and all it contains, if I had then said to you, *"No! You must NOT vaccinate your puppy,"* you might still not have taken any notice of me - because the brainwashing and fear of distemper, parvo, etc., and the desire to attend shows and training classes, and put dogs in kennels, is often stronger than the fear that your dog might be one of the so called 'tiny minority' of dogs who suffer adverse vaccine reactions.

I had a conversation over dinner with a girl who bought her vaccines for £5 from America and injected them herself. I was so frustrated by her delight in the money she was saving, that I ended up saying "you are killing your dog on the cheap" - very unlike me. But she went ahead and did it anyway, and the dog ended up very ill. I don't know the final outcome.

We are so brainwashed into believing the men in white coats that sometimes it takes something like this to make us stop and think. Lisa, it took the death of two dogs before I wised up. And call me mad, but I honestly and fervently believe that Oliver and Pru, and now Sam, came to this earth to save others. Zulu did the same. I don't know what you do, but I believe there is something in you that will do something very positive as a result of Zulu's sacrifice.

You will be going through a lot of emotions now. Anger, grief, guilt - all these are normal emotions experienced when you lose someone you love. Don't feel guilty, because you went to a lot of trouble to try to come to the right decision. It could have been that Zulu would have been fine - but sometimes Fate has a way of putting us on a certain path. I believe that the path you are now on will be extremely positive in the long run. As for Zulu, he has gone to a far better place. I also believe that you will meet him again.

The next time someone comes to me asking whether they should vaccinate, I can tell them about Zulu. Just think of the lives he will save. But for now, be kind to yourself and allow yourself to grieve. Do you know, when I took Pru for her last vaccine shot, she rolled her eyes in her sockets and climbed up on my back. I took no notice of her, and told her it was OK, the vaccine was good for her. How I regret that decision. But the larger picture is that hundreds, maybe thousands, of dogs will be spared our pain as a result of me letting Pru down. It's a hard burden to bear, but who said it had to be easy?

Catherine

I guess some clinical trials are required before anyone can say definitively that nosodes are effective against disease prevention, or that they are safe. I personally think they are as effective as vaccines, and have used them on my own dogs (as have hundreds of CHC members). But belief isn't good enough, is it. What's for sure is that the pharmaceutical industry isn't going to pay for nosode trials and homoeopaths often lack the funding to do so.

Ah well, another case of the more you know the more you know you don't know . . . So, in the absence of firm evidence, or confidence from homoeopathic vets, a balanced view might lead us to say:

1. Anecdotal evidence exists to support the use of nosodes
2. A small number of trials also support the use of nosodes
3. Nosodes should be given to healthy animals (as is also the case with vaccines)
4. Nosodes can be used in the face of an epidemic to, hopefully, halt disease
5. Nosodes do not guarantee protection, but they do offer evidence of a good level of efficacy
6. Vaccines come with known side-effects, and neither are they guaranteed to protect
7. Nosodes therefore represent a 'reasonable' alternative
8. Research funding is needed to study nosode efficacy and safety
9. It *may* be better to use nosodes in the face of an epidemic, rather than 'just in case'
10. Not enough is known about nosodes

On the other hand, my own homoeopathic vet, the wonderful James Newns, had this to say: 'Nosodes can do anything that a vaccine can do. I would recommend that animals are given nosodes early, at five or six weeks of age, to educate the stem cells. If the homoeopath is also vaccinating, nosodes can be used safely, providing they can get in first and the vaccinator uses drainage remedies to counteract vaccine damage. Unless the energy contacts a pathogen to latch onto, it can lead to problems.

'If using nosodes on their own without a vaccine, providing it's done properly by a homoeopath who knows what he's doing, pathogens the animal meets in the field won't develop. Being out in the world is quite enough for an animal – a vaccine isn't needed to give the animal the knowledge of how to overcome a challenge.

'Nosodes educate energetically, they don't go through the blood where problems can be caused. Properly made, maintained and understood, nosodes are safe and effective.'

Seven
The Healthcare War

Things are definitely coming to a head. I've felt it; everyone who has a position in the animal healthcare war seems to be feeling it, too. On the one hand I've seen homoeopathic vets under attack in the veterinary press; some of them have lost confidence in the homoeopathic nosode as an alternative to vaccinating. Perhaps, in some ways, they've lost confidence in themselves – it's easy to do that when you're under attack (but it's also possible to use the trauma to take another look and re-determine what is real).

God knows how conventional vets must be feeling at the moment. They're getting so much conflicting advice about the frequency of revaccination, and they have people like me (and I am by no means alone) saying that vaccines come with widespread side effects when, at one time, they were told that vaccines were safe. The vaccine industry is still saying they're safe. Then there are groups campaigning for independent monitoring of vets, and other campaign groups to alert dog owners to the side effects of various veterinary drugs.

I sense that people are confused, and many are frightened. They're trying to re-establish some kind of order, some kind of foundation that will settle all the confusion. It's no wonder, then, that the Veterinary Surgeon's Act is being re-drafted. On the one hand it looks as though vets are going to be regulated more openly, addressing many client complaints. On the other, it looks as though non-vets are going to be jumped on if they either diagnose or treat an animal. This has always been the law, but rumours say things are going to get quite unpleasant for anyone who is not a vet to involve themselves with animal healthcare.

Take a look at a snapshot of someone else's life, and see what is happening to them:

'My friend, who runs an online holistic pet supplies site, has had the Veterinary Medicines Directorate in touch recently. They say she cannot make any medicinal claims for any of the products. She can't say 'treat', 'treatment', 'dose', 'heals', 'prevents', 'clears', 'avoids', 'boosts', 'relieves, or 'remedy' – and I could go on. Neither can she mention any medical condition, like diarrhoea, but looseness is OK.

'She is not supposed to put any information about complementary therapies, nor link to any sites for that reason. I don't think they should be allowed to do this. They must be quite scared as more people are turning to natural remedies and the pharmaceutical companies may lose some of their huge income. Are they going to ban people from finding out about anything natural? You would think in this country that there would be the freedom of choice.'

The friend, the host of the web site, told me, 'I have spoken with one of my suppliers about the VMD, and they have had the same problems, maybe even worse. They have books for sale on their website and were told that they couldn't advertise these books as the titles contained 'medicinal claims'! I'm sure there must be some recourse under the Human Rights Act. The penalty is a £5,000 fine or six months in prison. Yet on the phone, the head of their section told me he was going to 'close me down'. Given they don't have the power to do so, I have asked them to provide evidence, in writing, of how they propose to do so.

'It seems very strange when the use of herbal remedies, homoeopathy, aromatherapy, etc., is completely legal, yet you are not allowed to make any reference to the uses of these remedies in connection with selling them, when there is plenty of information out there in books and on the net. Perhaps they want to totally ban all these things so that they can promote the chemical products instead.'

It seems ironic to me that the Veterinary Medicines Directorate is pouncing on natural products. Bearing in mind the drugs and chemicals they approve from the conventional realm, it's hard to understand how they can feel justified in doing this. I wrote the following article about flea control back in the early'90s. One of the chemicals mentioned in the article is Carbaryl. Within two weeks of the article being written, Carbaryl was withdrawn from use in children's head lice shampoos, whereas the VMD gave manufacturers a further 18 months to use up their stocks in dog flea shampoos.

FLEAS & WORMS

Fleas and worms go together, and this is the time of year when they worm their way in to your dog, or hop on board. Hedgehogs, rabbits, foxes, sheep - regular flea bags - and if your dog runs in fields inhabited by wildlife, or wildlife runs in gardens inhabited by your dog, then he has a good chance of picking these parasites up. So how do you prevent your dog from getting fleas and worms?

If you're like me, you might have nipped along to the vet, or the local pet shop, and bought some insecticidal shampoo. Except, when you are asked to write an article on the subject, you are duty bound to assess what it is you're evaluating.

So I looked through my copy of the "Compendium of Data Sheets for Veterinary Products". This is the vets' bible: it lists the products available from members of the National Office of Animal Health in the UK (a trade association). Members of the association prepare data sheets on each of their products, stipulating contents, use, directions, and contra-indications, and this is for use by vets when recommending or prescribing products.

I have to admit, I was shocked by what I discovered.

Shampoo

I found a nice turquoise coloured one with a lemongrass odour, containing Piperonyl butoxide and Pyrethrum. The Compendium doesn't tell you what the chemicals actually are, so I went to another book: 'C' is for Chemicals (Green Print, London), and this is what I found:

Piperonyl butoxide is 'highly toxic if absorbed through the skin, less so if swallowed. It has been shown to cause cancer in animals, although the US Environmental Protection Agency has concluded that it is not carcinogenic (will not cause cancer) to people'.

Pyrethrum is only moderately toxic if swallowed or inhaled, but it is an irritant and may cause allergic dermatitis or asthmatic breathing to sensitive people. Luckily, though, the same manufacturer sells an ointment for eczema and hot spots.

Then, whilst doing the weekly shopping, I stopped at the pet section and had a look at what Safeway had to offer. There were some jolly little flea collars that contained a chemical called Carbaryl. So I made a note and looked Carbaryl up when I got home. Apparently, Carbaryl is an insecticide with several garden uses, and it's good at killing fleas, too. Just the job then? The World Health Organisation lists Carbaryl as 'moderately hazardous'. It is a mutagen and it is carcinogenic and teratogenic in laboratory animals (this means it can cause mutations in cells; it can induce cancer, and it can cause birth defects when absorbed in pregnancy). Oh yes, and it's reported to be more toxic to dogs than to other animals.

Maybe those new-fangled little capsules might fit the bill? You know the ones - they protect your dog from reinfestation for up to four weeks. One of these, listed in the Compendium, contains Permethrin. So I checked Permethrin out in the other book, and the WHO considers Permethrin to be 'unlikely to present a hazard in normal use'. Phew! But the US Food and Drug Administration lists Permethrin as a possible carcinogen.

To be safe, the manufacturers suggest (in the Compendium) that your dog shouldn't be allowed to swim for twelve hours after treatment because the product is 'extremely dangerous to fish'. People shouldn't handle the treated area on the dog for three to six hours, and treated dogs shouldn't be allowed to sleep with people, particularly children.

So we mustn't get it on our skin, or let it into the waterways, or let our children near it, but it's ok for your dog to have it inside his body for 'up to four weeks'...actually, it kills fleas for up to four weeks - we don't know how long it remains in a dog's body.

Let's see...what else is there? Oh yes. Here's another one of these capsule thingies. This one contains an organophosphorous compound. According to 'C is for Chemicals', organophosphates are a class of chemicals, 'some of which are considered to be the most toxic chemicals ever manufactured.

But surely the manufacturers wouldn't use such dangerous chemicals on our dogs? Surely they use the harmless organophosphates? What is an organophosphate, anyway? "The high acute toxicity of organophosphates stem from their action against a vital enzyme in the body that regulates the functioning of the nervous system." Oh!

Fleas

So what about flea sprays? Here's a nice environmentally-friendly one: it doesn't contain CFCs, so it won't damage the ozone layer - good selling point! What does it contain, then? Answer: Dichlorvos.

The WHO lists Dichlorvos as 'highly hazardous'. It's poisonous if swallowed, absorbed through the skin, or inhaled. It is a mutagen and possible carcinogen and a potent anticholinesterase agent (blocking the transmission of nerve messages).

120

Rest assured, though, as the manufacturers state that the product is designed to have a high margin of safety. This is before the bit about 'if signs of toxicity appear administer the antidote atropine sulphate at 0.1-0.2mg/kg intravenously or intraperitoneally and apply artificial respiration'. Artificial respiration?! It's not the way they manufacture them, you see, it's the way stupid dog owners misuse them.

And my, aren't we stupid! I admit it. I have used some of these products, or products like them, on my dogs. I am angry. I trusted these manufacturers with my dogs' lives.

Of course, there are other ways of dealing with fleas and worms at the same time. Take garlic, as an example. I've been giving my dogs a clove of raw crushed garlic with their meals each day for nearly two years. We haven't had any flea infestations - but, of course, we don't have the benefit of science to tell us we're doing the right thing; besides which, you can't patent garlic.

There are other natural products said to be capable of keeping fleas and worms at bay : cider apple vinegar (from the health shop); raw meaty bones (yes, yes, I know they're supposed to give dogs worms - but you can't patent bones, so they would say that, wouldn't they?)

Those who promote the natural diet say that raw meaty bones help keep the immune system healthy, and a dog with a healthy immune system is no good to worms because, amongst other reasons, worms thrive on the mucousy toxic stuff that dogs with a poor diet accumulate in their intestines and guts.

So, if a chemical kills fish, doesn't kill dogs, but mustn't be allowed near people, or it's proven to cause cancer, but they use it anyway, what use is the laboratory data? And when you add that small dose of killing chemicals to all the other chemicals in the environment: the crop sprays, garden weed killers, disinfectants, plastics, mould treatments, and more - at what point is enough enough?

I'll leave you with this quote. It relates to human food, and we are only talking about dogs - they matter less than humans, don't they?

"The dispassionate objectivity of scientists is a myth. No scientist is simply involved in the single-minded pursuit of truth, he is also engaged in the passionate pursuit of research grants and professional success. Nutritionists may wish to attack malnutrition, but they also wish to earn their living in ways they find congenial." John Rivers. The Profession of Nutrition.

Finally, if you wish to use products on your dog, be sure you know what you're using and what the risks are. We are morally bound to make informed choices about the lives of our dogs - they don't have the choice, they simply have solutions imposed on them. Take care, for all life is precious.

A regulatory battle is waging in the human healthcare field. According to the Medicines and Healthcare products Regulatory Agency, part of the government's Department of Health in the UK, their job is to ensure that medicines, healthcare products, and medical equipment meet the appropriate standards of safety, quality, performance and effectiveness, and are used safely.

With regard to herbal remedies, the government's objective, they say, is that 'the public should have access to a wide range of safe, high quality herbal remedies with appropriate information about the safe use of the product. There needs to be a suitable balance between consumer choice and public safety.'

This sounds eminently reasonable to me. However, the campaigning group Consumers for Health Choice is concerned. It says that the Traditional Herbal Medicine Products Directive has been so substantially changed from the first draft that it will no longer help. 'Particularly at risk,' they say, 'are blends of herbs with vitamins and minerals, which the Medicines and Healthcare Products Regulatory Agency argues should be classed as medicines, requiring a full licence if the herbal ingredient is at therapeutic levels. The Directive 'would impose unduly onerous burdens on industry, for smaller businesses in particular and jeopardise the future of many safe, popular and effective herbal remedies.'

Of the Directive to amend the code of medicines, Consumers for Health Choice says, 'The European Union is currently considering a proposal to amend the main EU laws defining a medicinal product and setting out the licensing system for such products.

'This exercise . . . has been hijacked by the pharmaceutical industry. It is the pharmaceutical industry that is seeking amendments to the definitions of a medicinal product and to the scope of this Directive which, if accepted, would allow medicines regulators to insist that many food supplements were legally medicines, requiring a licence even if they are intended to be covered by other EU directives that define them as food products.

'This would lead at best to confusion about which regulations applied to which products, and at worst lead to perfectly legal and safe food supplements suddenly being reclassified as medicines having to comply with expensive and inappropriate licensing requirements intended for pharmaceutical drugs.'

The fear at ground level, amongst ordinary people who currently have the freedom to choose whether they will use conventional or alternative healing therapies and products, is that the multi-national, enormously wealthy pharmaceutical industry is seeking to have all natural products banned, so that we have no choice than to use their harmful drugs with unacceptable side-effects. The feeling is that we don't live in a democracy, but that big business tells our governments what to do.

The whole issue is compounded by the fact that many alternative therapies don't have a lot of scientific evidence to back them up. I know from experience, for example, that acupuncture was instrumental in restoring Gwinnie's ability to walk after she damaged a cruciate ligament. I know, from experience, that my conventional vet was flabbergasted when the aged Chappie's CDRM (a neurological condition which causes loss of movement in the back legs), improved after I gave him a herbal formula specifically for this condition. I know, because I saw it with my own eyes, that Emotional Freedom Technique physically altered Sophie's swollen deformed arthritic paws, turning them within seconds into non-swollen and non-deformed paws. I can't prove it to anyone.

I could, however, prove all of these things if I had the funding to conduct the relevant research.

Problem: who is going to give anyone money to research acupuncture or Emotional Freedom Technique? The large corporations certainly won't fund this type of research, because there would be no commercial benefit in doing so. Their money goes, instead, into research for drugs that will make profits for their companies. According to Consumers for Health Choice, it would cost around £250,000 to prove to the Medicines Control Agency that a substance is safe.

As for the herbal blend that helped Chappie's CDRM, if it costs £250,000 to gain approval per substance, then it would certainly cost over a million pounds to obtain approval for the blend. Will a corporation go to these lengths if the resultant product cannot be patented, since you can't patent naturally-occurring plant substances? Or are the multi-nationals going to alter the natural substances so that they can be patented? Many naturopaths fear this development, since they believe that Nature has designed perfection, which man can only disturb.

The other question is . . . how effective are the existing licensing regulations anyway? To some of us, it seems that they aren't working where pharmaceutical drugs and chemicals are concerned, so how helpful will it be to impose the same regulations on naturally occurring substances?

A small selection of many examples illustrates the point. We see news of this sort with such regularity that many of us are no longer shocked, and most of us feel that there is nothing we can do about it.

Sunday Times, 13th February 2005: 'Painkiller linked to hundreds of deaths'

'Doctors have reported 103 deaths (in the UK) they suspect were due to the painkiller Vioxx, which was withdrawn from sale over safety fears last September.

'The figures released by the drug safety agency also show there were 7,150 adverse reactions to the drug during its five years on sale in Britain.

'Experts say, however, that under-reporting through the government's 'yellow card' system could mean that the true death figure may be as high as 2,000 (in the UK).

'Vioxx was licensed in April 1999 with claims that it was safer than traditional painkillers, such as ibuprofen and diclofenac, for its main use in relieving arthritis.

'It was backed by a massive media campaign, often featuring middle-aged celebrities ice skating, and with a push to doctors through sales reps. In Britain about 10m prescriptions were written.

'However, evidence from studies sponsored by Merck Inc, its manufacturer, aimed at expanding the drug's use into other medical conditions, found a dramatic rise in heart attacks and strokes, prompting its overnight withdrawal. New Jersey based Merck, one of the world's biggest pharmaceutical groups, said its priority was patient safety.

'According to Merck, about 400,000 people were taking Vioxx in Britain when the company withdrew it worldwide. . . . Calculations based on the yellow card reports suggest that 2,000 patients may have died, a death rate of 1 in 400.

'The company disputed these figures this weekend but the calculations support those of Dr David Graham, an official in the US government's Food and Drug Administration (FDA), who became a whistleblower claiming that Vioxx was responsible for 140,000 heart disease cases and up to 56,000 American deaths.

'This week the FDA is to hold crisis hearings in Washington over Vioxx and similar drugs.

"In a huge number of cases, the benefit of these new drugs just wasn't worth the risk," said Professor Andrew Herxheimer of the UK Cochrane Centre in Oxford, who is one of Britain's drug safety experts. He believes that only about 5% of problems are reported through the yellow card system.

'Britain's notification arrangements by the Medicines and Healthcare Products Regulatory Agency are considered among the best in the world, but research reveals huge under-estimates. One survey found that only 16% of doctors had ever sent a yellow card, while another found that 80% of reports were filed by only 7% of doctors.

'Merck's UK subsidiary said that the figures had to be compared with those for traditional painkillers, which caused about 2,000 deaths a year.'

Ten of the 32 Food and Drug Administration (FDA) drug advisers whose total votes favoured the controversial painkillers Celebrex, Bextra and Vioxx had financial ties to the industry. According to public records and disclosures in medical journals, the 10 advisors had recently consulted with the drugs' makers.

At around the same time, the drug Co-Proxamol had to be taken off the market, because it caused depression and suicide in unacceptably high numbers.

These are drugs for humans – and we are told that human drug safety testing is far more stringent than it is for animals. The following report came from CNN Money during December 2004:

FDA slams Novartis on dog painkiller
'Novartis AG failed to give the government prompt, accurate reports about deaths of dogs treated with a painkiller in the same class of medicines now linked to heart problems in humans, US regulators have charged in a letter.

'Novartis (up $0.23 to $50.33) officials could not immediately be reached for comment.

'The drug, Deramaxx, is a COX-2 inhibitor approved for relieving arthritis and post-surgical pain in dogs.

'Similar drugs for people are under heavy scrutiny after studies associated them with heart attacks and strokes. One of the drugs, Merck & Co Inc's (up $0.33 to $32.23) Vioxx, was pulled from the market because of safety risks.

'Death has been reported in 'rare situations' when dogs were treated with Deramaxx, according to the drug's label instructions.

'The Food and Drug Administration, in a warning letter dated Nov. 29, said Novartis Animal Health Services should have forwarded complaints about deaths and health problems in dogs given Deramaxx within 15 working days, but in some cases delayed as long as 10 months. Some reports, including ones involving deaths, appeared to have incorrect dates, the FDA said.

"Novartis failed to submit timely and accurate information to the FDA regarding serious (adverse drug experiences) associated with the administration of its FDA-approved animal drug product Deramaxx . . . during its first year of marketing," the FDA said.

'The company also failed to submit proper information about post-approval studies of Deramaxx, the FDA charged. The drug is known generically as deracoxib.

'The FDA sends dozens of warning letters per year. Most of the issues raised are resolved without further regulatory action, although the letters sometimes lead to tougher steps such as product seizures.'

Rimadyl, also known as Carprofen and Zenecarp, another arthritis drug for animals, is also being questioned by animal lovers who claim that their pets died as a result of taking it. According to Pfizer's own datasheet for dog owners:

'Rimadyl, like other drugs, may cause some side effects. Serious but rare side effects have been reported in dogs taking NSAIDs, including Rimadyl. Serious side effects can occur with or without warning, and in rare situations result in death.

'The most common NSAID-related side effects generally involve the stomach (such as bleeding ulcers), and liver or kidney problems. Look for the following side effects that can indicate your dog may be having a problem with Rimadyl or may have another medical problem:

- Decrease or increase in appetite
- Vomiting
- Change in bowel movements (such as diarrhea, or black, tarry or bloody stools)
- Change in behavior (such as decreased or increased activity level, incoordination, seizure or aggression)
- Yellowing of gums, skin, or whites of the eyes (jaundice)
- Change in drinking habits (frequency, amount consumed)
- Change in urination habits (frequency, color, or smell)
- Change in skin (redness, scabs, or scratching)'

Over a hundred animal owners joined together in America to mount a class action lawsuit against Pfizer, the drug's manufacturer. The FDA ordered Pfizer to produce a datasheet for animal guardians (some of which is shown above), stipulating clearly that death was a potential side-effect of taking this drug.

In other countries, the legislators have not asked that Rimadyl come with such information for pet owners. Indeed, at a recent Foundation in Canine Healthcare course, a vet who had just finished her final year at college told us that she had been taught about the drug in college, but not about the side-effects. Much of the information, though, will be in the datasheets prepared for vets, but I suspect that many vets are too busy to look at them.

The Senior Dogs Project – www.srdogs.com - has done a great deal of work to help dog owners with regard to Rimadyl. They do not damn Rimadyl, but believe that information should be available to dog owners so that they can work with their vets to make their own choices about their friends' healthcare. The following exchange from the Senior Dogs website illustrates how some vets believe such information should be censored.

"Your list of deaths of dogs on Rimadyl read like something from National Enquirer. I feel you are doing a disservice to many people by even allowing these anecdotal contributions be put on this media. 'AIHA caused by Rimadyl.' 'Eleven year old Doberman paralyzed by Rimadyl.' To what do you attribute the greater number of cases of AIHA (3-4 year old female Cockers) who are not on Rimadyl? The Doberman most likely had a cervical disc problem which would not and probably could not have been successfully treated. I was recently blamed for a 17 year old dog with a brain tumour going into renal failure after I prescribed Rimadyl for hindlimb arthritis. The owners were anxious to blame me after reading your list of totally nonsupported anecdotal list of deaths. If you are determined to allow these cases to be available on your site, please pay for post mortem exams and publish those as well. I am a general practitioner and doubt that many clients will be prepared to pay for monthly CBC's and chemistries but they sure are happy when their old dogs act young and happy again when they start taking Rimadyl or Etogesic."

The reply:

"Dear Dr.:
"Thank you for contacting us. We sincerely appreciate knowing your views on the srdogs website's coverage of Rimadyl. We fully understand your concern and frustration, and wish we were not in the time-consuming, burdensome, and equally frustrating position of providing a public forum on an issue that has created so much controversy and concern among consumers. The issue is of concern not simply because dogs have suffered side effects from Rimadyl; we state repeatedly in our coverage of Rimadyl that all drugs have side effects and that the risks of taking a drug must be balanced against the benefits. The issue has arisen because: (1) consumers have been led to believe that Rimadyl has no serious side effects; (2) information about side effects is not being made available to them when the drug is prescribed: and (3) veterinarians, themselves, in a number of the cases reported, have not been aware of the drug's side effects, contra-indications, or drug interactions.

"FDA guidelines on adverse drug experiences clearly state that an ADE report may be filed when there is a suspicion that a drug is implicated. We are following the same guidelines. Another important guideline we follow, however, is to compare the reported incidents with the potential side effects listed in the Rimadyl product description published by Pfizer. The two conditions you cited in your message -- AIHA and paralysis -- are, in fact, noted by Pfizer as potential adverse side effects in the product description. (They are mentioned under the heading "Adverse Reactions ...... Post-Approval Experience.") We screen out reports that present symptoms other than those listed by Pfizer, such as those we have received in which cancer and heart disease are mentioned. Clearly those could not possibly be related to Rimadyl.

"Our list of 'anecdotal' material is not, as you describe it, 'totally nonsupported.' Many of the deaths and toxic reactions presented in the reports on srdogs have been determined by Pfizer vets themselves to have been related to Rimadyl. We sincerely regret that your clients would blame you for their dog's renal failure on the basis of information on the srdogs website. However, 'acute renal failure' is, in fact, one of the adverse reactions noted by Pfizer in the product description. Both the product description and a consumer-oriented sheet entitled 'Important Information about Rimadyl' are supposed to be given to a client when Rimadyl is prescribed. Thus, you see, the information is available in a source other than the srdogs website and, according to Pfizer's own directives, should have been made available to any of your clients whose dogs were taking Rimadyl.

"Pfizer has ordered and paid for necropsies in a number of Rimadyl-related cases. We would be more than happy to post on the srdogs website any necropsy reports Pfizer would care to forward to us, particularly in those cases in which the necropsy indicates that Rimadyl played no part in a dog's death. We realize that there are very few people who would be in a position to pay for monthly CBCs. That is an idea proposed by the FDA's CVM - not by us. We felt, since it was an advisory issued by the CVM about a drug that is under discussion on the srdogs website, it made sense to post the information.

"Again, we deeply regret that your clients accused you of harming their dog by prescribing Rimadyl, and sincerely hope that you have been able to repair your relationship with them. We also hope you might consider that any information can be misused, and that it is not the presence of the information itself that is at fault.

Respectfully yours,
The Senior Dogs Project'

I may be presenting a biased and contentious view when I say that, in my view, it seems that the licensing system is enabling unsafe drugs to get to market, and that the drug companies have their own ready-made sales team in conventionally-trained doctors and vets, who have been educated by a system that takes money from the self-same companies. But before pharmaceuticals get to the sales team, the drug companies have allies in the form of government officials who believe it is acceptable to rely upon research that has been solely funded and directed by the companies producing the products. If viewed in this way, the licensing system doesn't protect us and our pets, but it could have the opposite effect.

According to an e-news broadcast in March 2003 issued by the excellent magazine *What Doctors Don't Tell You*: 'The Medicines Control Agency is the UK's drugs licensing authority. It's there to protect the consumer against dangerous pharmaceutical drugs, and to pull any drug that might be causing harm.

'It also happens to be one of the most secretive organisations in Britain. Its meetings are held in secret, and no minutes of proceedings, apart from revealing the names of attendees, are ever made public. Any members who would dare step out of line and reveal proceedings to the press could face two years' imprisonment if the information compromised a drug company and its work.

'The National Audit Office has been investigating the workings of the MCA and has concluded that the drug licensor needs to communicate better with the public (or at all, come to that) and to become more transparent.

'It's also discovered that not only is the public unaware of the MCA's responsibilities, but also even health professionals are unclear of its duties. Worse the introspection of the MCA is so complete that its warnings about drugs are sometimes ignored by the manufacturer, often with impunity.

'Perhaps this is all to do with the funding of the MCA. It is one of the few drugs agencies in the world to be entirely funded by . . . the drugs industry. (Source: *British Medical Journal*, 2003; 326:119).'

The Sunday Express goes further. In November 2001, it reported: 'Many Government advisers on the safety of medicines have close financial ties with the pharmaceutical giants who produce the controversial measles, mumps and rubella jab. A Sunday Express investigation has found that nearly a third of the 181 experts who sit on the Medicines Control Agency (MCA) committees are linked to GlaxoSmithKline, Aventis Pasteur or Merck, Sharpe and Dohme.

'51 members either hold shares in these companies or are dependent on them for consultancy fees or research grants. The MCA has continued to endorse the triple measles, mumps and rubella (MMR) jab despite concerns linking it to autism and stomach disorders. But the extent of the MCA members' financial ties to MMR manufacturers raises questions about potential conflicts of interest.

'Liberal Democrat health spokesman Nicholas Harvey said the matter should be looked into. "If these experts have pecuniary interests in the companies, we can't be confident they are making objective decisions," he said.

'Members of the MCA are also concerned. Joe Collier, Professor of Medicines Policy at St George's Hospital Medical School in London, said many committee members are too close to drug companies. He claims there is an "institutional bias" which makes the experts ready to take the industry's point of view. Health experts also argue that MCA meetings are secret and therefore not open to public scrutiny.

'Jackie Fletcher, from the campaigning group JABS, which is highlighting the possible health risks of MMR., said: "Monitoring bodies keep saying that they are independent but what is the definition of independence when they have shares and interests in the companies that manufacture and distribute the vaccines?"

'The size of the members' shareholdings is confidential because they are not required to disclose on the MCA's register of interest how many shares they own. But our research - based on drug companies' share registers from April last year - found several experts have substantial investments. Dr Michael Denham, a retired consultant in geriatric medicine and a member of the committee on Safety of Medicines External Advisory Panel, owned £250,000 worth of shares in GlaxoSmithKline. Professor Roderick MacSween, a professor of pathology at Glasgow Western Infirmary, had nearly £26,000 worth of shares in Glaxo-SmithKline. Dr Michael Donaghy, a brain specialist at Oxford's Radcliffe Infirmary Hospital, who sits on the MCA had £19,000 worth of shares. 11 professors and doctors have received fees for research from Aventis Pasteur.'

I think it's worth quoting John Bradshaw again: 'As we humans act in repetitious ways, necessitated by circumstances relating to survival, these repetitions become habitual. These habitual behaviours soon become socially acceptable ways of behaving. They are socially agreed upon. After a while these socially agreed upon habitual ways of behaving become what sociologists term 'legitimised'. After being legitimised for a while, they become unconscious. The unconscious legitimisations gradually evolve into *laws of reality*. We no longer question them. We accept them: they are predictable. They insure our security. If someone tries to change them, we get very upset.'

I have included only a very small number of examples to illustrate that the drugs licensing system isn't working. In fact, it appears to me that very few, if any, regulatory systems appear to work.

Jan Mahoney and Felicity Norton in the UK recently formed a group called Animal Aid to call for better monitoring of the veterinary profession. They have been in contact with terrible cases of professional misconduct - a vet who performed surgery in his kitchen, with inadequate anaesthesia and unqualified support; a vet who kept a dog with a life-threatening pyometra (womb infection) in a cage for more than 18 hours (delegating the surgery, for the next morning, to a junior vet, who didn't feel confident to perform the spay, and who waited until the boss returned - the dog died soon after); a vet who gave a cow wormer to a tiny Yorkie pup, causing it to haemorrhage and die; the list goes on and on. It is thought that it isn't helpful to have the veterinary profession policing the veterinary profession, and Animal Aid seeks to rectify this error. Similar concerns have hit the media with regard to doctors policing doctors.

But what about us? What is our role, as clients, in all of this? Isn't it also our responsibility to assume that regulatory authorities aren't on the spot all of the time, to watch what is happening, all of the time? Isn't it up to us to discriminate about the vets or doctors whose advice we call upon? Or, basking in the false security of these systems, are we making false assumptions about safety? Are we allowing ourselves to be disempowered, just because someone else has qualifications after their name, or sits on a fancy committee (and who has usually been chosen to sit on the committee because he shares the belief system of the committee on which he sits).

Above we have examples of government committees being staffed by people with financial ties to the companies whose products they are meant to protect us against. This happens all around the world. There are laws and procedures in place to prevent errors arising because of this, but generally, in my experience having addressed many of these issues directly at government level, they are often waived and overlooked. Commercial influence is accepted; it is a *law of reality*.

And now they're bringing natural herbs and vitamins into the regulatory sphere. The fear is that the regulations will be guided by the pharmaceutical companies who either want to wipe out the health competition, or who want to use their money and power to alter and patent natural substances so that they can become even more profitable. This may or may not be the case. My concern is that human beings ought to have a right to study, examine, and adopt the best methods of healthcare that they themselves deem are right for them and their loved-ones. Laws should be designed to protect society, not to tie our arms behind our backs so that we are helpless in the face of extreme corporate power.

Please be clear on one point: whenever anyone raises a concern that the public needs to be protected against faulty products or services, they tend to say that they are concerned for *others*. Most people who want to censor information or limit choices feel confident that they can make their way through the minefield themselves. They just don't have confidence in anyone else being able to do it. This is an argument that parallels the movement to ban printing presses when they were first invented, since knowledge in the hands of the ignorant *might* have led the world into terrible trouble. It seems very arrogant to assume that everyone else is stupid – they are not. Consider the following example where a 'stupid' pet owner was able to speak out for the positive benefit of her dog. Nick Mirabelle wrote:

Last March Zoomer came down with bacterial Pneumonia and Septicaemia. We took the dear old lad into the vets on a Friday evening. Our regular vet was away and would not be back until the following Thursday. The substitute vet was one that we had used before, but we were not enthused with his approach. This time he kept insisting that Zoom had Leukemia even when Vicki insisted that it seemed more like Pneumonia.

He ran the usual tests and found that Zoom's white cell count was down to 2.57. Normal would be more between 12 and 18. Again the "L" word was used and again Vicki insisted on Pneumonia. The vet wanted to keep him over at the hospital and Vicki said no. If he was going to pass on she wanted him at home where she could care for him. The vet insisted again that he needed to be on an I/V and best would be to leave him. Again Vicki insisted that she bring him home and that he, the vet, load her up with the necessary bags of I/V fluid and antibiotics. The vet, Vicki insisted, should put a heparin lock in Zoom and she would do the rest. Fortunately he complied . But, the vet tended to speak more to me during this time rather than directly to Vicki. You see, Vicki's Mum was an RN and Vicki grew up with Gray's Anatomy. Vicki has a penchant for caring for animals and she does her research. Vicki has scores of books on the shelves these days where she goes as soon as there is the smallest sign or symptom that something is not quite right.

Zoom came home with us that night and, thanks to Vicki and her willing Zoom to live , he is still here in spite of the vet. I went in on the following Sunday and picked up reloads on the I/V drips and antibiotics. From that Friday night for the next three weeks our front room looked like an Army Field Clearing Station. An old floor lamp was pressed into service as a I/V stand and we put Zoom on a mound of beds with incontinence pads (Hospital bed pads) under him. Vicki nursed Zoom, we fed him and took him in to our regular vet on the following Thursday. The first thing our vet said when looking at the X-rays of Zoom's chest was " He has a terrific case of Pneumonia"! Of course, Vicki went through the overhead. The good news was that we made the right decision in insisting on antibiotics and drip I/V. We also made the right decision to get him home and take care of him ourselves.

No one was putting much money on Zoom to last much beyond that Spring. But, here he is today. Zoomer has had another bout with Pneumonia, but, happy to say that he came through with flying colours. Zoomer's worst enemy at this time is his age. Zoomer started out life with a bad Thyroid, bad hips and was , in fact rather oversized for a Clumber. His body structure was a bit tall, long, and lanky. But, Zoomer , in spite of his bad Thyroid and a very bad auto-immune system has persevered for these many years. Irregardless of all Zoomer's physical shortfalls, he was blessed with the most loveable nature. Vicki has always referred to Zoom as her "Gentle Old Soul". Today, Zoomer thrives especially when he smells food. Generally Zoomer prefers citrus fruits, but he will most certainly devour whatever is handy such as pears, apples, bananas, etc. He has been known to devour four Avocadoes at one sitting (stolen fruit of course) (you might say the " fruits of his crime"). After he was caught in the sitting room on the peach coloured carpet , which was tinted green at this point, he looked up sheepishly and burped as if to say " Sorry Dad, but I couldn't help myself". There was no way that either one of us could get angry at that mug!

But, enough of stolen fruit and other canine misdemeanours. There are many stories about Zoomer which we would like to tell. Most certainly, one day there might even be a Zoomer book. Zoomer by himself could inspire many people to press on and to have a much brighter outlook on life. His attitude is to keep your eyes on the bone! The real reason for writing this is to expand on the narrative about the vet and Zoom's bout of Pneumonia last March. We both firmly believe that Zoom would never have made it 1) If we had left him in the care of the Vet, 2) Zoom would not be here today if it were not for Canine Health Concern, 3) Zoom would not be here today if it were not for a healthy, raw and natural diet as well as his vitamins and supplements.

After Scooby's death and the death of another Clumber Spaniel placement whom we had for only 4 months, we turned to CHC on the recommendation of a friend. Thanks to all the information and assistance that has come from the e-mail list and the CHC newsletter as well as advice and assistance we have received from fellow CHCers, and of course, Catherine, your book we have turned to BARF and have never turned back.

Our regular vet knows what we do and how we do it. She has told us that she does not approve of feeding raw to the dogs or cats. But, over the years that she has seen Zoomer and suddenly saw our number of trips to them drop greatly (with anywhere from 6-9 dogs at any given time) she had to comment that whatever we are doing to keep on doing it. We have a very good rapport with this vet and have brought in some of your newsletters as well as other bits of information and a list of reading material for her to look at. Vicki has helped her out on several occasions to find remedies and solutions to problems which she otherwise would not have considered. I don't know that we will ever 100% convert her to " our" side. But we at least have her better than 50% there now.

Thus, between Zoomer's great attitude (where's the food?), his stamina and perseverance, Vicki's dogged determination and all the help, advice and nurturing that we have received from you and CHC, Zoomer is still here well beyond his original life expectancy. Many years ago some very close British friends used the term " Keep your Pecker up!". On this side of the Ocean it has a bit different meaning.

135

Needless to say, not only has Zoomer pressed on, but he has kept his pecker up!

When we originally got into Clumbers by way of getting Lance as a puppy (Lance as it turned out later is Zoomer's son) the life expectancy of a Clumber at best was 10 years. Zoomer was 7 1/2 as was Scooby when Scoob passed away. We expected Zoom to last no more than another 6 months after that. Little would we have expected Zoomer to be pushing 13 1/2 now and still having a relatively good life even though his mobility is not good.

It is time to end this epistle. I just want to say in closing that thanks to your philosophy we have been able to give such a Gentle Old Soul a good life and in return he has given us dedication, devotion, and love far greater than we could ever imagine or expect from such a creature.

I think perhaps that the word 'love' is key to Nick and Vicki's wonderful letter. This couple love the animals, and nothing and no-one will stop them pursuing their loved-ones' best interests. How, then, can we justify legislating away people's ability to make choices based on love?

I am consciously going to use a very strong word to explain what I think of the effect of some lawmakers and licensing authorities: *abusive*. They are abusive because they seek to exert control on people who neither need nor want their control. You, of course, are free to disagree with the word I have chosen to use, although I would ask you to examine my reasons for using this word.

I am also going to use the same word to describe my feelings about the system that empowers certain individuals, who have studied in a very prescribed way, to ignore the experience and knowledge of others who have not limited themselves to the organised system of healthcare – and who fail to consult with their clients and seek consent. Toni Nyquist, an 'ordinary' dog lover who works for lost and abandoned dogs, wrote to me:

I work with animal rescue. I cannot begin to tell you how many dogs are not only over vaccinated by rescue process but many shots are done by foster homes 'to save money'. I refused to do that myself even though they provided the vaccines, which usually sat in the bottom drawer of my fridge until they expired.

A friend recently picked up a dog she adopted and called me in a tizzy. She said while she was there, the foster volunteer gave her dog an all-in-one and then said rather offhandedly, 'Oh, uh-oh, here's a sticky showing she already had one - oh well - it won't hurt her'. My friend was very upset about this. I advised her to try to contact a local vet who might be able to give her a nosode for the over vaccination.

I had an Irish Setter who had been with me for a year. He developed the rolled eyelid problem that is a problem with setters. I took him to my vet to have the surgery done on his eyelids. (I found out later there was a homeopathic way to help this). While my Riley was UNDER ANESTHESIA, the vet vaccinated him. He said he 'noticed he was not up to date'. When I found out he had done this I was very upset. I told him the dog had a three year rabies and had his other vaccines done elsewhere. He apologized and said he would not charge me. But, I asked, can you take the stuff out of his system? No.

Riley developed seizures that started that evening. They were erratic and mild but Riley seemed to know they were coming. He would go to his bed, an open kennel, lay on his side, brace his feet, go through the seizure, and recover. He was the sweetest most loving Setter and I felt so sad that I had messed up his life by not telling this vet the dog had vaccines. But I did not expect the vet to act on his own without asking me first. I did NOT give him permission to do anything but the eyelid surgery, which by the way did not work.

I also adopted a deaf pup from a local shelter. She had been adopted out three times in a two month period and returned because, even though people were told she was deaf, they could not deal with her. Each time she was brought back and adopted out again, she was given shots again. Can you imagine, that poor up, over a period of two months, had that many vaccinations? My point here is she developed diabetes and eventually had to be put to sleep because she also developed a tumour in her abdominal cavity. I lost Holly Noel, my heart dog, at the age of seven. It should not have happened. It was not fair to her.

Abuse doesn't need to be overt in order to be abuse. Abuse can also be covert. Much of the frustration and confusion of the human race stems primarily from our attempts to control the reality of other people and from letting their reality control us. A person's reality is made up of the body, thinking, feelings and behaviour. *Positive* control is when I determine my own reality apart from the reality of others. With positive control, I establish for myself what I look like, think, feel, and do and not do. As a healthy person I am in control of my reality, of knowing what it is, embracing it, and expressing it when it's in my best interest to do so – as Nick and Vicki did. Positive control is the opposite of negative control.

Negative control of reality happens whenever I give myself permission to determine for another person what he or she should look like, or think, feel and do or not do. On the other hand, allowing someone else to control me is also negative control. Whenever I fail to determine for myself what I look like, what I think, what I feel, and what I do or don't do, and allow someone else to control any of those things for me, I am participating in negative control.

When people have impaired boundaries (the ability to distinguish themselves from others), it is impossible to tell where one's reality stops and another's begins. Because there is no respect for the other person's individuality, and no comprehension of another's ability to think for themselves, we think we can tell others how to think, feel and behave.

Personal *physical* boundaries enable human beings to refrain from tampering with others, either sexually or physically. Society, on the whole, accepts our physical rights these days: we have learnt that it is OK to ensure that others keep their physical distance from us without worrying about the perpetrator's comfort, but of our own comfort. We mostly feel able to take care of ourselves by telling others how close they can stand to us, or whether they can touch us or not. We are yet to catch up, as a species, on the importance of internal boundaries.

People with a damaged or nonexistent internal boundary believe they are entitled to tell you what to think, feel, do, or not do; *or* they believe that they must let you tell them what they should think, feel or do. This is a sicknesses in our society that the vast majority of us believes to be 'normal'. It is not.

Our internal boundaries protect our thinking, feelings and behaviour, and keep them functional – doing the job they were meant to do, as Vicki demonstrated on behalf of Zoomer. When we are using our own internal boundary, we can take responsibility for our thinking, feelings, and behaviour, and keep them separate from those of others. With internal boundaries, we can also stop blaming others for what we think, feel and do. Our internal boundaries also allow us to stop taking responsibility for the thoughts, feelings and behaviours of others. This allows us to stop manipulating and controlling those around us.

Some of us, as children, were never taught how to have internal boundaries; we were taught to find fault with others, for example. In this way, children 'learn' to regard others as inferior to themselves. Other dysfunctional family systems actually teach their children that they are superior to other people, giving them a false sense of power. Nationalism has the same root. Such people have problems with personal relationships: they have difficulty accepting that others are entitled to have their own reality or say 'no' to them.

Conversely, some parents disempower their children by telling them what they must think, feel and do. They disempower them by 'loving them too much' – not teaching their children how to take care of themselves physically (like showing the child how to cook or wash), or emotionally and intellectually by not trusting the child, at the appropriate developmental stage, to make their own choices. Instead, they do it all for them. The result is adults who can't take care of themselves, can't make their own decisions, and who are open to abuse.

When we have no internal boundaries, we have no sense of being abused or that we are being abusive. Such people may have trouble saying 'no' or protecting themselves. They allow others to take advantage of them physically, sexually, emotionally, or intellectually without realising that they have the right to say, 'stop that'. They may also exert their will upon others when it is not appropriate to do so – because they have no concept of another's right to think, feel and do as they choose. This is what makes victims and abusers in our society. Solve this issue, and we would resolve most of the crime issues.

What makes one-to-one relationships work also makes systems (groups of people joined together through a shared interest or aim) work. There has to be some level of equality, where the reality of each individual is respected. Kahlil Gibran said in *The Prophet* that the victim is never innocent of the crime. We need, if we wish our society and the people and animals in it, to be healthy, to get our heads around the fact that we cannot leave all the thinking and decision making to an elevated few; to someone else. Neither can we dictate these things to others – we cannot morally do it because we are not the ones who live with the consequences.

It does not work, for example, to have vets acting as the superior members of the animal healthcare system, because clients are equal members of the system (they are, after all, the ones who pay the bills, and they are the ones the animals look at with love and trust in their eyes. Furthermore, clients often have 10, 20, 30 and 40 years of experience of raising animals behind them). It is not just unfair for clients, it is also unfair to vets – because clients, having abdicated any responsibility in the process, or having had it wrested from them, sure as hell go looking for someone to blame when their pet dies, and that person to blame is the vet who was made, or allowed himself to be made, into a Power Higher than the other members of the system. This is especially so with the vaccine issue, since there is so much confusion and so little consensus in this area.

Neither does it work to have 'superior' individuals decide which healthcare products or natural substances we can and cannot use. It doesn't work for the reasons mentioned above – the system is susceptible to corruption; the licensing authorities have difficulty exerting control over the manufacturers of drugs; and products go to market only to be withdrawn after thousands of deaths have occurred: it's not working.

Now, will someone please tell me why it is better to impose a system that isn't working than to allow individuals to use their own ability to study, research, read and think? We all make mistakes, this is what it means to be human. When we set ourselves up as someone who has the ability to make choices for others, we place ourselves outside the realm of being human – we think we are gods. We are not. This belief system is faulty. We need to look at our beliefs in this respect. We need to empower our fellow human beings to be all they can be, and not disempower them by telling them that they cannot.

The following news item appeared in Sun Journal, Maine, USA on the 1st March 2005:

A public hearing Monday on a proposal to mandate consumers be given information about the risks and benefits of vaccines turned into a face-off, with no agreement between veterinarians and pet owners.

Veterinarians staunchly opposed legislators forcing them to give pet owners information about vaccines. They're already doing that, they said. And the science about adverse health risks from vaccines is "fluid," making it impossible to give good information, veterinarians said.

Pet owners and dog breeders who jammed into the standing-room-only hearing were on the other side of L.D. 429. They questioned why veterinarians were so opposed to giving out information.

With her little dog, Minnie, in her arms, Laura Moon of Brunswick said she favors the bill. Everyone was there because they love animals, she said. "That's why I think disclosure is so important. How as an owner, as a guardian, do you know if you don't know?"

When any activity raises potential harm, precautionary measures are warranted, even if the cause and effect are not fully understood, Moon said. "How can we make an informed decision if we don't have information?"

Joan Jordan, a dog breeder and dog obedience teacher from Woolwich, said she's seen dogs "that have had a vaccine that had had lumps and died. Personally I had a dog a couple of years ago I lost." Weeks after her dog had a vaccine, she underwent surgery and chemotherapy, she said, adding that 18 months later "Sarah" died.

When humans are prescribed medicine they're given information about possible risks, Jordan said. "I see no reason why the veterinarians feel that that's a threat to their services. ... What's the problem with us just knowing what the research is saying?"

Arnold Woolf of Lewiston, a breeder and dog judge, called the bill a "safeguard for dogs and cats." Years ago he sold a Collie puppy to a couple who took that puppy to their veterinarian. That veterinarian "re-inoculated the animal," giving shots the puppy already had. The dog died within 48 hours from a vaccine overdose, Woolf said. " That's what the autopsy showed."

Veterinarians disagreed that the bill would do any good. They testified about how critical vaccines are to keeping dogs and cats disease free, how their profession is under attack with inaccurate information.

Dr. Bill Bryant of Winthrop, past president of the Maine Veterinary Medical Association, said veterinarians are strong proponents of education, but they're against the bill. Vaccine protocols have changed and will continue to change, he said. Experts disagree on the science of health risks, he said. With that science "fluid," Bryant asked who would write information in disclosures, and what set of research would be used?

Legislators should not mandate disclosure forms "for what is a rapidly evolving national veterinary issue that Maine veterinarians are actively addressing," Bryant said.

Dr. Paul Wade of Manchester said polls show that veterinarians are among the most trusted professionals. Wade said he gives his clients numerous consent and information forms on many services, including vaccines, that show the benefits and side effects.

Most veterinarians are also doing that, he said. "There is no need for a state law to force us to do something we're already doing voluntarily. The bill is not a legislative issue," Wade said with a tone of annoyance. "The hidden agenda behind this bill is not for the protection of welfare for animals, but an attempt to further control an already ethical and trusted profession."

This news item demonstrates that veterinarians do not wish to be controlled by legislation. This is understandable, since no-one wants to be controlled. We all want to be free to use our own judgment. The fear might also be that pet owners will make 'ill-informed' decisions and expose their pets to the risk of contagious disease. Back to the printing presses, again, and keeping the public protected from making mistakes. Unfortunately, as I have shown you elsewhere, *everyone* makes mistakes, and legislation merely seems to ensure that BIG mistakes are made in a BIG way.

Added to this, vaccines are not guaranteed to protect, other forms of preventative healthcare (like nutrition) might work better, vaccines come with known side-effects, and individuals are known to withstand disease even if they are not vaccinated. No one should, knowing this, dictate anything to anyone. Pet owners are asking for information to be available so that they can make their own decisions and live with the results – which we all do when we stand vigil as our animals die. Vets, in the above news item, appear to be resisting this, seeing it as an attempt to prevent them from making the ultimate decisions about pet healthcare, no doubt based upon the belief that they know more than us.

Please do not conclude that I am attacking vets. I am not. I am looking at the system which keeps the bombs flying on both sides of the healthcare war, and the beliefs which light the fuse. It is not about Them and Us, vets versus animal guardians. The truth is that we are all of us human beings who have no need, and no moral right, to control one-another. If we worked together, then the power of the pharmaceutical industries would be broken, and our pets' lives would not be determined by big business, for good or ill. We would be working and learning and growing together, in a state of peace. Importantly, our ability to see the truth would be strengthened.

I am telling you now about Edward and Daniel because it is the truth, and not because I wish to go one up on anyone: These two dogs are nine years old, and their health is a constant source of amazement to me. They have received no vaccines, ever; they are fed naturally (ie no processed food). When I took Daniel to the vet for a checkup last year, at the age of eight, there were no veterinary records for him. Edward, having been attacked by another dog, and having strained his foot whilst charging through the heather, does have records. They contrast sharply with my vaccinated pet-food-fed dogs, who were at the vet's every two weeks with one problem or another. I attribute this contrast to the fact that I took my dogs' healthcare into my own hands. I stepped into my power and studied and searched for knowledge that would enable me to better care for my friends.

I now work with my vet, I do not obey my vet. We are both human beings, learning together. In addition, I am blessed with the support of James Newns, a homoeopathic vet who uses hair samples to assess my dogs' health, and who sends remedies to prevent illness arising when required. Emotional issues are resolved using Emotional Freedom Technique (which anyone can learn to do, and which uses no drugs and no manipulation, but energy to heal.)

If I were a vet, I can't help thinking that it would be such a joy to be part of the team that educates and empowers animal guardians, so that they and their animals can enjoy good health and the wondrous light of understanding. What a wonderful vocation that would be. Instead of resisting the inevitable, vets would be part of the team that is currently helping humanity to evolve. Oh wow. What a brilliant future it will be.

Eight
Let Food Be Thy Medicine

Vaccines come with unquantified risks and no guarantee of protection; nosodes come with a paucity of research to support their use. Proper nutrition, however, does give us a positive way in which we can influence health for the better.

I am told that, in the horse world, people are moving away from the manufactured feeds, even though they might have herbs thrown in (which my friend Sally Spencer, author of *The Morgan Horse,* tells me cannot be applied on a one-size-fits all basis). Now, informed people are going back to natural feeding for horses, which means mirroring the grazing and roaming process as much as possible (which can mean limiting *natural* food when the horse cannot roam), and giving herbs therapeutically and discriminatively.

In the cat world, many are seeking to mimic what a cat would eat if given the choice in the wild. This means delivering what a small prey would deliver: raw white meat and a very small amount of vegetable matter, as found in the stomach content of prey.

Tom Lonsdale, a wonderful vet who has sacrificed his career in order to campaign to return carnivores to their natural fare, believes that dogs, cats and ferrets should be given a diet mostly based on raw meaty bones – whole carcasses, a small amount of vegetable matter, and some table scraps. Unlike Tom, Ian Billinghurst – another raw meaty bone vet - believes that carnivores should also be given supplements. Juliette de Baircli Levi, the pioneer in holistic healthcare for dogs, advocated the feeding of grains and raw meat to dogs. Pat McKay, another expert, believes that grains for dogs are not a good idea. Ann Martin, who wrote *Food Pets Die For* believes that raw meat is dangerous for dogs, that we should cook their food. And the big multinationals believe that their complete and balanced commercial food in a can or a bag is, um, all your dog will ever need.

After many years of lapping up all of the advice on what to feed my dogs, I believe that all of the above are right! Even though they disagree with one-another to a greater or lesser extent. I suppose I'm in trouble again.

My reason for agreeing with them all is based upon the following exceptional experiences.

After Oliver and Prudence died, and my other dogs were suffering from thyroid disease, arthritis, allergies and autoimmune disease, I read an article in an Australian dog magazine about raw meaty bones for dogs. It was as though a lightbulb went on in my head: I had been starving my dogs to death with a complete dry dog food that wasn't sustaining life. I immediately switched my dogs to the raw meaty bone diet, and my dogs thrived. Our vet bills dropped by 65% and, when we surveyed CHC members who had switched their dogs to the RMB diet on our advice, they reported an 85% drop in veterinary visits. People wrote to us to tell us how healthy their dogs were on raw food – glossier coats, more vitality, skin problems clearing up, lovely clean teeth, clean breath, and in some cases, medication was no longer required. We were so enamoured by the positive changes in our dogs' health, that we invested a great deal of time and money in promoting raw feeding for dogs. That diet is now used by thousands of delighted animal guardians around the world.

I believe this to be true: the vast majority of carnivores thrive on the food that Nature has designed over millions of years to sustain life. That is, prey animals like rabbits, rats, deer, mice, lambs, hens, and so on, *uncooked*. Dogs, being scavengers, also thrive on eggs, berries, fruit and the food that they might find in the prey's stomach, such as grains and vegetable matter. You should see Edward on walks around the country estate we live on. He picks raspberries from the bushes and jumps to pick apples from the trees. He also enjoys catching and eating rabbits.

One day, something happened to modify my view. My friend Sally Cronk came to visit for a week, bringing her German Shepherd Etta with her. Etta hadn't eaten raw meaty bones before, but Sally was keen for her to try the natural diet. So Etta had raw chicken wings alongside my own dogs. When Etta got home, Sally had to take her to the vets, where she stayed for several days on a drip. The reason, it transpired after some deduction, was that Etta could not tolerate the energy – the life force – in raw food. Countless generations of breeding and artificial food had modified the dog so that she could not tolerate real food.

Then, when my own Sophie reached the age of 15, she started to develop diarrhoea. I tried everything to help her: homoeopathic remedies, antibiotics, herbs – all to no avail. I happen to be extremely fortunate in that I have a friend who is a medical intuitive who is also very knowledgeable about canine health. In desperation, I telephoned her on Sophie's behalf, only to be told that Sophie could no longer, at her great age, tolerate the energy in raw meaty bones. I was advised to switch Sophie to a tinned senior dog food and, after a while, I could revert to real food, but this time cooking it for Sophie. Gosh darnit, but my friend was right. Principles were thrown to the wind, and the tinned food halted Sophie's diarrhoea. After a while I was able to cook her chicken, white fish and vegetables, and she lived to a good age of 17.

Then I read about a dog in the media who made it to 21. Unbelievably to me, this dog had been a vegetarian since she had been rescued as a puppy! Her owner phoned me one day so I was able to ask questions: the dog wasn't vaccinated every year, but her owner was a serious vegetarian who studied the protein requirements of her canines and gave them the nutrients they needed by adding vegetable protein sources to the diet.

Another lady came to me with her aggressive dog. The dog was eating a dry food and I wondered whether this might be the source of the problem (since some of the commercial processed foods can provoke aggression in dogs). After much deduction, it transpired that this dog actually did very well on the dry food. Her owner had tried raw, but the result had been huge digestive upset. The difficulty, it transpired, was that the dog wasn't sure of her place in the family, and she was behaving aggressively to balance-out her owner's overly meek behaviour.

So once again I will repeat: most dogs thrive on a natural raw diet, with some rare exceptions.

Quite a few years ago I was invited to attend and speak at a holistic dog camp run by a wonderful woman called Wendy Volhard. Wendy's knowledge and understanding of canine dietary requirements is awesome. Her knowledge is backed by around forty years of science: she has consistently advised her followers to take blood samples for analysis from their dogs, enabling them to ascertain whether the diet is producing health or ill-health before unwanted consequences arise.

Most importantly, Wendy advocates muscle testing so that owners can work out the specific dietary requirements of their animals. And so do I. Some dogs, it transpires, fare better with lamb than beef, others better with chicken than lamb, and so on. Just like humans, dogs are not all uniform in their requirements. No individual, of whatever species, is anything other than unique.

Take a simple example: some humans (and individuals of any species) need more food than others. We know this because some lucky blighters can eat anything they like and stay slim. Others who try to get away with eating the same amount pile the weight on. Rob and I are a prime example (sob). We walk the dogs together, so our exercise levels are pretty similar. Rob is like his mother and I, sadly, am like my mother. Genetically, Rob is skinny, and I am not.

Our dogs, Edward, Dannie and Gwinnie, also have differing dietary requirements. Gwinnie is prone to putting on weight – she gets less to eat than the boys, much to her disappointment. She also fares better on white meats and good amounts of vegetable matter. Dannie tests positive for high purine foods, like beef and liver. Edward, bless him, at the age of nine, needs to avoid high purine foods.

Edward's limbs ache in the evenings, showing symptoms somewhat like gout.

Gout is caused by an excess of uric acid in the body. Uric acid results from the breakdown of purines. The excess can be caused by either an over-production of uric acid by the body or the under-elimination of uric acid by the kidneys. Also, the ingestion of foods high in purines can raise uric acid levels in the blood and precipitate gout attacks in some 'people'.

According to the American Medical Association, purine-containing foods include anchovies, sardines in oil, fish roe, herring, yeast, organ meat, beans, peas, mushrooms, spinach, asparagus, and cauliflower. Foods that may be beneficial to people with gout, however, include dark berries, white meats, fatty acids, salmon, and white fish. A herbal blend containing garlic, artichoke, turmeric, milk thistle and yucca can help lower uric acid levels in the body. Aloe vera and vitamin C can also reduce inflammatory reactions in the body. Basically, Edward needs more vegetables and fruits than Dannie does, and supplements that Dannie doesn't need. This is reflected by the fact that Edward helps himself to fruit in the environment, and Dannie doesn't. When I eat an apple, Edward wants some; Dannie isn't interested.

This isn't to say, of course, that we should always follow our, or our animals', likes and dislikes when it comes to food. I just love chocolate and puddings, but these aren't necessarily foods. They are

147

designed to excite the palate – different function. We can also be addicted to the foods we are allergic to.

This is why I believe we all need to find a diagnostic tool to help us work out the best diet for ourselves, and for our animals. Then, once we have established the best diet, we need a rudimentary understanding of using foods as medicine (since they can't legislate food away from us, even though they might try to rob us of our right to use vitamins, minerals and herbs therapeutically).

I am not going to tell you in this book how to dowse or muscle test. The reason for this is that I don't believe you can learn it on a page. You need to find someone to teach you, in person. Actually, I'm offering you a precious gift: the chance to go and meet interesting and knowledgeable people who are a little further along the road than you. You'll get direct proof that dowsing and muscle testing is more than airy fairy unscientific nonsense. You'll find it works. In a year or a few months, you will be where they are now: you'll be your own expert. Go to your local health shop and ask them to recommend someone who is a Kinesiologist or a dowser. Ask around. You will find them near you. Enrol on a course or have a few one-to-one sessions. We do, incidentally, teach both muscle testing and dowsing during our Foundation in Canine Healthcare course.

There are also many books on animal nutrition which you can read. These are given in the recommended reading list. I would, however, like to illustrate some broad concepts for you to consider. It is, if you like, the skeleton over which you can add the meat.

The first consideration is quality. You need to mix the quality (energy) of the diet with the energy of the animal. Consider the following news story which attained national coverage in the UK a few years ago:

Condemned meat conspiracy exposed

BBC News Online: UK
Thursday, 21 December, 2000

Five people have been found guilty of selling hundreds of tonnes of pet food as meat fit for human consumption. Environmental health officers from Rotherham Council - who uncovered the fraud - say

1,300 tonnes of condemned meat was sold to butchers, supermarkets and restaurants all over the UK. The prosecution said it had caused an "incalculable risk to human health".

Containers of smelly, badly-bruised poultry, covered in faecal matter, flies and feathers, were found by investigating officials. Inspector Gary Blinkhorn, of South Yorkshire Police, which investigated the fraud jointly with Rotherham Council, said it was a "heinous crime".

"I am a police officer but also a family man with children and an elderly mother and I would not want chicken from these people on their plates," said Insp Blinkhorn. You only have to look at food poisoning outbreaks in hospitals to realise that something like this could kill people. After a five-year investigation which has cost a lot of money, I am extremely pleased with today's three guilty verdicts."

Nationwide fraud denied

A jury at Hull Crown Court found Andrew Boid, 33, of Carlton, Nottinghamshire, Darren Bibby, 29, of Oldcotes, Nottinghamshire, and Peter Tantram, 47, of Ingham, Lincolnshire, guilty of conspiracy to defraud businesses by selling poultry not fit for human consumption. They had denied the nation-wide fraud, which operated between 1993 and 1996 and earned millions of pounds. Before the trial began in September two men had already pleaded guilty to the fraud.

They were Arnold Smith, 63, of Sheffield, and John McGinty, 48, of Woodsetts, near Rotherham, South Yorkshire. All five are due to be sentenced on Friday. The jury found Timothy Powell, 38, of Hove, East Sussex, not guilty. The jury failed to reach verdicts on Tantram's wife Louise, 45, Boid's father Clive, 55, of Worksop, and Kevin Wilson, 39, of Cleethorpes, North Lincolnshire, and were directed to find all three not guilty.

The jury heard that Clive and Andrew Boid and Bibby were bosses at Newark-based company Wells By-Products Ltd, which was responsible for processing poultry meat for pet food. Its main customers were pet food giants Spillers and Pedigree.

The company bought in huge quantities of condemned poultry, which was packaged as pet food and invoiced to Lincoln-based company Cliff Top Pet Foods, run by Peter and Louise Tantram, the court was told.

149

The meat was then cleaned up and passed on to a man not on trial, who helped change the product's identity from pet food to normal food, said prosecutor Ben Nolan QC. The profits made from the operation were enormous and ran into millions of pounds over the three years, Mr Nolan said.

Salt and slime

The scam was uncovered when food officials launched an undercover surveillance operation on a company in South Yorkshire. Large quantities of salt, used to remove slime from the meat and freshen up its appearance, were discovered in addition to the smelly, badly-bruised poultry. Seized invoice books showed butcher shops, supermarkets and restaurants across the UK were being supplied. Clive and Andrew Boid and Peter Tantram were also found guilty of conspiracy to sell pet food-grade meat, which was falsely represented as human food quality to Pedigree. Rotherham environmental health officer Lewis Coates, who led the authority's investigation team, said there was evidence that the trade in unfit poultry meat had existed since the late 1980s

"This investigation was potentially only part of a much wider problem," he said. "As it proceeded officers became aware that similar scams were operating throughout the country. Despite what we found, no-one followed up our findings and we feel that a full investigation into the extent of this illegal trade should be undertaken."

Senior council officers are meeting officials from the Food Standards Agency early in the New Year to discuss the national implications of the case.

So what we can deduce from this news article is that the standards applied to human food are not applied to pet food. Slimy, smelly poultry, capable of causing an incalculable risk to human health, is OK for dogs, it seems.

If you look at the side of many pet food cans and packets, you will see descriptions of content. These include phrases like 'meat byproducts', 'derivatives of a vegetable origin', and various 'approved' additives. This basically illustrates that food that is fit for human consumption goes into the human food chain. As the men in the dock demonstrated, you can earn more money for human grade food than you can for pet grade food. This is not to say, of course, that there aren't pet foods on the market which contain better quality ingredients. They do exist, and it is up to you to satisfy yourself that, should you choose to feed food especially prepared for animals, it meets your own quality requirements.

Also bear in mind that if you pay a dollar or a pound for a quantity of meat, then you are getting a dollar or a pound's worth of meat. If you pay a dollar or a pound for food in a can or packet, you are also paying for canning, packaging, manufacturing, and a huge marketing budget. In some instances this can amount to tens of millions of pounds spent on advertising by one pet food company in one year. The resultant value of the food in the can or packet is going to be a lot lower than the intrinsic value of a relatively unadulterated slab of meat on a butcher's counter.

Consider also the fact that the chemicals and additives allowed into human food are far lesser than those showing up in pet food. The following news report is but one of many examples of the fact that if you don't make it yourself, you don't really know what's in it:

The American Food and Drug Administration (FDA) announced that almost half of all the dog food tested for pentobarbital showed the presence of traces of the drug. The FDA insisted dogs were not in danger by eating food with traces of pentobarbital in it.

"While it may not have an immediate effect, there really is no telling what will happen over time, which could cause some liver complications," says Dr. Jay King, a veterinarian.

The FDA survey, which was conducted by the Centre for Veterinary Medicine, included popular brands chosen at random. Out of four samples of Ken l Ration tested, all of them showed traces of pentobarbital. Out of 11 samples of Ol' Roy dog food tested, six showed traces of pentobarbital. Out of seven samples of Heinz dog food tested, three showed traces of pentobarbital. And out of 24 samples of Purina products, three showed traces of pentobarbital.

The FDA says the pentobarbital probably came from disabled or diseased horses and cows, which are euthanised and rendered and allowed to be used in pet food products. Despite suspicions that pentobarbital may come from euthanised dogs and cats from animal shelters, the FDA says DNA tests on the products show no sign of dogs or cats. The FDA also says just because the samples showed traces of pentobarbital in 2000, does not mean the products currently on the shelves contain pentobarbital.

Despite all the qualifiers, some veterinarians say they're still concerned about the presence of pentobarbital in some pet food.

"None of us want to think that our animals are eating these foods with these chemicals in them even as a small or trace amount. So, yes, it is a source of concern," says Dr. Teresa Garden of the Humane Society.

The FDA refused to be interviewed about the tests, agreeing only to answer written questions. When asked whether it will continue to allow pentobarbital to be in dog foods, the office says it "does not intend to take any further actions."

Dog food makers won't be forced to monitor pentobarbital levels and won't be forced to notify consumers of the presence of pentobarbital. The FDA says, "Manufacturers must list ingredients they deliberately add to pet food. Because pentobarbital is not deliberately added, it does not need to be listed on the label."

All the pet food companies referred all questions to the Pet Food Institute, which also declines to be interviewed. In a faxed statement, the institute writes, "Consumers purchasing dog food made by Pet Food Institute members can feel confident they are feeding their pet a safe and nutritious food."

Hmm… The American Food and Drug Administration doesn't believe that traces of pentobarbital in food could pose a danger to dogs. Americans can rest safely in their beds, knowing that the government licensing authority is looking out for them and their pets.

According to JM Loveridge plc, manufacturer of Pentobarbitone (same thing, different name), however, 'Pentobarbitone is a potent hypnotic and sedative (Schedule 3 poison). It is toxic if swallowed and can be absorbed through the skin. In case of accident the following action should be taken:

Skin: Wash immediately with water and then thoroughly with soap and water.
Eyes: Irrigate immediately with cold water and obtain medical aid.
Accidental self-inoculation: Seek URGENT medical attention, advising medical services of barbiturate poisoning. Do not leave

patients unattended. Maintain airways and give symptomatic and supportive treatment.

Ingestion: Obtain medical aid at once. Wash out mouth. Keep warm and at rest. Administer symptomatic and supportive measures. The concentration of pentobarbitone in the product is such that the accidental administration of quantities as small as 2ml can have serious CNS effects. It is reported that a 1g dose could be lethal to humans.

Hazard warnings: i) Toxic (Schedule 3 Poison) (Skull and Crossbones Symbol)

ii) In the event of accidental administration to an animal not presented for euthanasia, measures such as artificial respiration and administration of oxygen, and the use of analeptics are appropriate.

Now the FDA might be quite right: your dog might be absolutely fine with a daily dose of traces of a barbiturate. But some of us would like a choice, which means (current 'protective' bodies notwithstanding) we have to source our own ingredients.

Consider also the relationship between the food you give to yourself and your animals, and the ability you and your animals will then have to combat illness.

In the early 1900s, Sir Albert Howard CIE, MA, Honorary Fellow of the Imperial College of Science, Former Director of the Institute of Plant Industry, and Agricultural Advisor to States in Central India and Rajputana, provided us with a wonderful example of the importance of good husbandry.

Sir Albert had a small farm in India of seventy-five acres and six pairs of working oxen. He was anxious to select his own animals, to design their accommodation and to arrange for their feeding so that he could see what the effect of properly grown food would be on the well fed working animals, and how such livestock would react to infectious diseases.

Sir Albert's animals were very carefully selected for the work they had to do and for the local climate. Everything was done to provide them with suitable housing and with fresh green fodder, silage and grain, all produced from fertile soil (it was actually the quality of the soil which caused him to conduct his experiment, since his interest lay in growing plants).

The oxen soon began to be in demand at agricultural shows – not as competitors for prizes, but as examples of what an Indian ox should look like. Sir Albert's aim was then to watch the reaction of these well chosen and well fed oxen to diseases like rinderpest, septicaemia, and foot-and-mouth disease, which frequently devastated the countryside and sometimes attacked large herds of cattle maintained on the Pusa estate. Sir Albert declared, 'I always felt that the real cause of such epidemics was either starvation, due to the intense pressure of the bovine population on the limited food supply or, when food was adequate, to mistakes in feeding and management.

'The working ox must always have not only good fodder and forage, but also ample time for chewing the cud, for rest, and for digestion. The grain ration is also important, as well as a little fresh green food. Access to clean fresh water must also be provided. The coat of the working animal must also be kept clean and free from dung.

'The next step,' he said, 'was to discourage the official veterinary surgeons who often visited Pusa from inoculating these animals with various vaccines and sera to ward off the common diseases.'

Sir Albert then deliberately brought his animals into contact with diseased stock. This was done by allowing them to use the common pastures at Pusa, on which diseased cattle sometimes grazed, and to come in direct contact with foot-and-mouth disease. The latter was easy, since Sir Albert's farm was only separated from one of the large cattle sheds of the estate by a low hedge over which the animals could rub noses, and he saw this happening many times.

Nothing happened. His oxen did not contract foot-and-mouth, or any other disease. This experiment was repeated year after year between 1910 and 1923.

Sir Albert maintained that the most complete demonstration of the principle that soil fertility is the basis of health in working animals took place at the Institute of Plant Industry at Indore, where twenty pairs of oxen were maintained. Again, great care was taken to select sound animals, to provide them with a good water supply, a comfortable, well-ventilated shed, and plenty of nutritious food, all raised on humus-filled soil. The result of this was a complete absence of foot-and-mouth and other diseases for a period of six years.

But this is not the whole of the foot-and-mouth story. When the 300 acres of land at Indore were taken over in the autumn of 1924, the area carried no fodder crops, so the feeding of forty oxen was at first very difficult. During the hot weather of 1925 these difficulties became acute.

A great deal of heavy work (stress!) was falling on the animals, whose food consisted of wheat straw, dried grass, and millet stalks, with a small ration of crushed cotton seeds. 'Such ration might do for maintenance,' said Sir Albert, 'but it was inadequate for heavy work.'

The animals soon lost condition and for the first and last time in Sir Albert's 25 years in India, he had to deal with a few mild cases of foot-and-mouth in some dozen animals. The patients were rested for two weeks and given better food, when the trouble disappeared never to return. This warning stimulated everyone concerned to improve the hot-weather cattle ration and to secure a supply of properly made silage for 1926, by which time the oxen had recovered condition.

Sir Albert Howard's experiences, covering a period of twenty-six years at three separated centres, convinced him that foot-and-mouth disease is a consequence of malnutrition, and that the remedies adopted to deal with foot-and-mouth in places like Great Britain, namely the slaughter of the affected animals, are both superficial and inadmissible.

'Cases of foot-and-mouth disease,' said Sir Albert, 'should be utilised to tune up practice and to see to it that the animals are fed on the fresh produce of fertile soil. The trouble will then pass and will not spread to the surrounding areas. Foot-and-mouth outbreaks are a sure sign of bad farming.

'How can such preventive methods of dealing with diseases like foot-and-mouth be set in motion?', Sir Arthur asked. 'Only by a drastic reorganisation of present-day veterinary research,' he said. 'Instead of the elaborate and expensive laboratory investigations now in progress on this disease, which are not leading to any practical result, a simple preventative trial on the following lines should be started:

'The animals should be carefully selected to suit the local conditions and should first of all be got into first-class fettle by proper feeding and management. Everything will then be ready for a simple experiment in disease prevention. A few foot-and-mouth cases should be let loose among the herds, the reaction of both healthy and diseased animals being carefully watched.

'The diseased animals will soon recover. There will most likely be no infection of the healthy stock. At the worst there will only be the mildest possible attack which will disappear in a fortnight or so.'

Nearly a hundred years on, and is anybody listening? I suppose those of us who pay the vet bills, and who see animals as people who are worthy of our love and attention might listen. From Sir Albert's experiments, we can make the following deductions:

1. Obtain the best genetic stock (although his experiment did not seek to see what might happen to cattle that didn't appear to be genetically superior).

2. Feeding the best, biologically appropriate, food is essential in preventative healthcare.

3. If the nutrition is correct, animals don't need vaccines.

4. Soil fertility, ie soil that is not depleted of 'humus' (decomposed organic matter) will produce nutritious food.

5. Animals who are working hard (stressed) need better quality food.

6. Foot-and-mouth disease, and by inference other pathogenic diseases, are a result of malnutrition (inappropriate husbandry).

7. Forget spending money on expensive scientific trials – feed the animals properly.

8. Forget potential ineffective and harmful vaccines – feed the animals properly.

The basic principles of correct feeding are:

Feed, as much as possible, what the animal would eat in its non-domesticated state. Observe your animals. Good health will ensure they are:

- Full of vitality, but neither over- nor under-active
- Well-coated
- Sweet-smelling
- Resistant to parasitic, viral or bacterial infection
- Supple in movement

- o   Good natured (neither aggressive nor timid)
- o   Sound in digestion (neither constipated nor prone to diarrhoea)
- o   Well covered (neither too fat nor too thin)
- o   Free from itching and scratching

It is also worth mentioning the now-famous Pottenger's Cats study. In this, a scientist called, interestingly, Pottenger, raised some 700 cats over several generations and observed what would happen to them with a small change in diet. The cats who were fed raw meat, milk and cod liver oil thrived over generations. The other cats, who were fed exactly the same, except their meat was cooked, became sicker and sicker over generations. Apart from eventually producing mutant kittens and becoming infertile, the cooked-food cats became susceptible to parasites and, you've guessed it – pathogens (disease causing agents such as viruses).

I have learnt to observe animals energetically which, in quantum physics terms, means that you are able to see disease in the energetic sphere before it manifests physically. That is, I look at the energy emanating from the animal. This can tell you most of what you need to know. A healthy animal shines from within. A malnourished, vaccine-damaged animal has trouble dragging his weary body around. Usually their owners will think a dog like this is healthy, but it is possible to learn how to look. Other animals are wound up tight, like brittle coils, waiting to spring. When an animal is healthy, you expect to see serenity combined with vivacity; the ability to totally relax com-bined with the ability to become alert and sparky at the right time.

To achieve this state of balanced energy, animals – and humans – need a good body to inherit, appropriate fuel, freedom from toxins, and an absence of emotional discord (stress). Life is never perfect, but it can be fun and rewarding to aim for perfection.

In the quest, you become knowledgeable, and this is fun and very interesting. Consider, for example, nutrients, their functions, and their deficiency symptoms on the following pages, and also how many of them respond to cooking, freezing and processing. According to the American government's animal feeding guidelines, no-one actually knows the full vitamin and mineral requirements of dogs – but this will give you a basis (based mostly on human study):

Vitamin	Functions	Deficiency Symptoms	Best Food Sources
A	Sight,skin, mucous membranes, anti-infective, protein synthesis, bones, anti-anaemia, growth	Spinal infections, respiratory infections, scaly skin and scalp, poor hair quality, poor sight, burning and itching eyes, dry eyes	Halibut liver oil, liver, butter, cheese, eggs
B1	Helps convert glucose into energy in muscles and nerves	Easy fatigue, muscle weakness, loss of appetite, nausea, digestive upsets, constipation, irritability, depression, poor memory, lack of concentration	Brewers yeast, brown rice, wheatbran, oatflakes, liver, wholemeal bread
B2	Helps convert protein, fats and sugars into energy. Needed to repair and maintain body tissue	Bloodshot eyes, tired eyes, light sensitivity, cracks and sores in corners of mouth, hair loss, trembling, insomnia, slow learning	Brewers yeast, liver, cheese, eggs, wheatbran meats, yogurt, milk, green vegetables

Vitamin	Functions	Deficiency Symptoms	Best Food Sources
B5	Production of energy. Production of anti-stress hormones. Controls fat metabolism. Formation of antibodies. Maintaining nerves. Detoxifying drugs.	Loss of appetite, indigestion, abdominal pain. Respiratory infections. Fatigue, insomnia, depression, psychosis, headaches. Puppies starved of B5 died when vaccinated	Brewers yeast, pig liver, pig kidney, nuts, wheatbran eggs, poultry, meats, whole-grains, beans, vegetables
B6	Needed for formation of brain substances and nerve impulse transmitters. Blood formation. Energy production. Anti-depressant, anti-allergy.	Inflamed tongue, inflamed nerve endings, migraine, mild depression, irritability, swollen abdomen	Brewer's yeast, wheatbran oatflakes, pig's liver, bananas, wholewheat, nuts, meats, fatty fish, brown rice, potatoes, vegetables eggs
B12	Needed for synthesis of DNA, the basis of all body cells. Maintains healthy myelin sheath. Detoxifies cyanide in food and tobacco smoke	Sore tongue. Nerve degeneration causing tremors, psychosis, mental deterioration. Menstrual disorders, pernicious anaemia	Pig's liver, pig kidney, fatty fish, pork, beef, lamb, white fish, eggs, cheese, spirulina algae

Vitamin	Functions	Deficiency Symptoms	Best Food Sources
C	Anti-oxidant, iron absorption, healthy collagen, resistance to infection. Controls blood cholesterol levels. Activates folic acid. Produces anti-stress hormones. Produces brain and nerve substances	Weakness, muscle and joint pains, irritability, bleeding gums, gingivitis, loosening of teeth, haemorrhages in skin, eyes, nose	Rosehip syrup, blackcurrant parsley, kale, horseradish, broccoli, green peppers
D	Promotes absorption of calcium and phosphate from the food	Delayed ability to stand, bone pain, muscular weakness and spasms, brittle bones	Cod liver oil, kippers, mackerel, canned salmon, tuna sardines, eggs, milk
E	Antioxidant, reduces oxygen needs of muscles, maintains healthy blood vessels	Irritability, water retention, haemolytic anaemia, lack of vitality, lethargy, apathy, lack of concentration, muscle weakness	Cod liver oil, shrimps, olive oil, vegetables pulses, tomatoes, meats, fruits

| K | Control of blood clotting | Usually in newborn, and include: excessive bleeding from stomach, intestine, umbilical stump | Cauliflower, green veg liver, beans, tomatoes, meat, potatoes, |

Vitamin	Stability in Foods
A	Insoluble in water so does not suffer loss through processing and cooking in water. Oxygen in foods destroys vitamin A, which is accelerated by peroxides and free radicals formed from fats in the food. Peroxides and free radicals are in turn formed by high temperatures, oxygen and light.
B1	Very unstable. Principal losses of thiamine are due to its water solubility. The more finely ground the food the greater the loss. Cooking meat at up to 150 degrees C causes no destruction but considerable losses into the juices. At temperatures of 200 degrees, 20% of thiamine is destroyed.
B2	Easily destroyed by light. Stable to oxygen, acid and heat up to 130 degrees. Readily lost by leaching in wet processing and cooking. Light in the presence of alkali converts riboflavin to luiflavin which destroys vitamin C.
B5	Easily destroyed, even in deep freezer. Destroyed by heat
B6	Very stable, losses occurring in boiling milk
B12	Light may destroy some proteins. Leaching represents main loss in food preparation.
C	Most unstable of all the vitamins. Up to 70% lost in cooking. Losses from light and oxygen.
E	Very unstable. Very sensitive to oxidisation. Losses occur from freezing. Processing and refining of cereals lead to wholesale losses of vitamin E. Cooking and processing in fats destroys up to 90% of the vitamin. Boiling destroys up to 30% in some vegetables.

161

	Canning even worse.
K	Some losses in commercial processing, including deep freezing.

Mineral	Functions	Deficiency Symptoms
Cobalt	Used in the synthesis of vitamin B12.	Loss of appetite, reduced growth, loss in body weight, followed by emaciation, anaemia and death.
Copper	Essential for haemoglobin formation, enzyme systems, hair and bone development, pigmentation, reproduction and lactation.	Fading hair, coat light. Nervous symptoms, lameness, swelling of joints, fragility of bones, anaemia
Iodine	Essential for the production of thyroxin (a hormone which controls the rate of metabolism/heat production) in the thyroid gland.	Goiter in calves, lambs and kids. Stillbirths, weak young. Known as cretinism in young animals, myxedema in adults.
Iron	A constituent of haemoglobin - the iron containing molecule that transports oxygen in the blood and other enzymes involved with oxygen transfer.	Anaemia - fewer red blood cells and lower haemoglobin levels
Managenese	Essential for normal bone formation, growth and reproduction. Activator of enzyme systems involved in oxidative fatty acid synthesis and cholesterol metabolism.	Poor growth, lameness, shortening and bowing of the legs, enlarged joints, testicular degeneration in males and impaired ovulation in females.

Selenium	Involved in vitamin E absorption and retention.	Liver function, resistance to disease, anti-toxic, sexual reproductivity, healthy eyes, hair, skin; anti-inflammatory, healthy heart, may protect against cancer, anti-oxidant
Silicon	Involved in the mineralisation of bones.	Essential component of cartilage, blood pressure control, contained in connective tissue
Sodium	Maintains osmotic pressure and acid-base balance of body fluids which in turn regulates nutrient transfer, waste removal and water balance in body tissue. Plays a role in muscle contraction and in the production of bile.	Reduced growth and feed utilization. Reduced milk production. Weight loss in adults. Infertility in males. Delayed sexual maturity in females.
Chlorine	Maintains osmotic pressure and acid-base balance of body fluids. Component of gastric juice (hydrochloric acid).	Retarded growth.
Calcium	Bone and teeth development. Nerve function. Muscle contraction, Blood coagulation. Cell permeability. Milk production	Rickets in young. Bone pain, muscle weakness, twitches and spasms

Phosphorus	Bone and teeth development. Is a constituent of phospholipids required for lipid transport, metabolism, and cell membrane structure and RNA and DNA required for protein synthesis. Also a component of several enzyme systems.	Rickets in young. Osteomalacia in adults. Depraved appetite (pica). Breeding and urinary problems.
Magnesium	Essential for normal skeletal development. Is a constituent of bone, and functions as an enzyme activator in the glycolytic system. Helps decrease tissue irritability.	Flushing of the skin. Hyperirritability, loss of appetite, convulsions and death.
Potassium	Plays a role in muscle activity, carbohydrate metabolism and enzyme reactions involving creatine.	Retarded growth, muscle weakness, unsteady gait, pica, diarrhoea, distended abdomen, emaciation followed by death.
Sulphur	Constituent of cystine and methionine (amino acids), biotin (for lipid metabolism), thiamin (for carbohydrate metabolism) and coenzyme A (for energy metabolism)	Retarded growth due to insufficient protein synthesis.

My aim here is to illustrate that, with the correct nutrients in our bodies, health is more likely to be assured. Many people and animals are being given drugs with harmful side-effects when proper feeding would resolve the problem, rather than the symptoms. Many, many Canine Health Concern members, and even those who are not CHC members, have taken charge and adapted their animals' diets to resolve chronic illnesses. Some of us now have elderly dogs whose health records have been astoundingly good, having got the basic husbandry right.

Many readers will already have adopted natural diets for their animals. In my experience, we converts are always more than willing to share the good news of what we now know. You may even be reading this book because a 'born again' dog, cat or horse owner lent it to you or suggested you get yourself a copy. We may not have money to pay for fancy TV advertisements, but we do have enough enthusiasm and love for the animals to ensure that word of mouth will triumph, and the animals will continue to get healthier.

In addition to CHC's Foundation in Canine Healthcare course, there are many resources to help you find the right diet for your animals. Books abound, and there is also a wealth of internet discussion groups for enthusiasts to learn and share their knowledge.

Discriminate with regard to where you go to find your knowledge. If it's sponsored by a pet food manufacturer, for example, then the emphasis is likely to be slanted to promote the company's products. Local colleges of education also run animal husbandry courses, although in my experience they tend to teach what they have been told, so the received wisdom could be overly-reliant once again on commercial data. Bizarrely, people who have qualifications after their names to say that they are animal nutritionists also have a tendency to be overly-influenced by commercial pet food companies, and many of them act as consultants to them. This is not necessarily a bad thing, but it might produce people who recommend something from a can or a packet.

As a word of caution, please research natural diets before you jump in, and please research the use of vitamins and minerals before you add them to your animals' food. You don't have to be a brain surgeon to know how to feed your animals, but it is possible to give nutrients in excess which can cause nearly as many problems as not giving enough. Balance in all things.

Please also notice that I'm not telling you to consult a properly qualified professional (who may or may not have all the answers) but to use your own inner powers of reading, listening, researching, and becoming knowledgeable in your own right. Take your time, have confidence in yourself, and step into your power. There are many books available which give clear and detailed guidelines on animal feeding, many of which are listed at the back of this book – it's up to you to choose the optimum diet for your individual animals.

Nine
Genetics

When I first started Canine Health Concern, most people complaining about the state of our dogs' health blamed the breeders. Everything, they said, was due to 'irresponsible breeding'. I couldn't really relate to that statement, because the people who bred Oliver, Prudence and Samson were amongst the loveliest people I had ever met. They loved the dogs with a passion, and they were certainly not irresponsible. True, the system of showing and breeding might have its faults – but I couldn't see how it was reasonable to blame individual breeders for all the ills of the canine world.

It's interesting to look at genetic faults in dogs, though, since we have manufactured specific breeds and are able to examine the concentrations of genetic problems. German Shepherds are known to have poor immune systems, for example; Golden Retrievers are genetically predisposed to allergies and tumours; Shelties are genetically predisposed to be nervous; West Highland Terriers are predisposed to atopic dermatitis (inherited skin problems); Cavalier King Charles Spaniels are known to suffer from heart conditions; Flatcoats are known as 'the cancer dog'; Rottweilers appear to suffer from neurological conditions, and so on.

In the dog world, many screening schemes exist involving x-rays for musculoskeletal problems, including hip dysplasia, Wobbler's syndrome, and Legg-Perthes disease. Within the nervous system, the ears and eyes come in for genetic screening. The cardiovascular system is a common area for genetic defects in dogs, and there are many schemes to try to weed out these problems. Blood abnormalities such as Von Willebrand's disease can also be screened-for. Hypothyroidism is commonly diagnosed in dogs, and this is known to have a genetic base. Ultimately, though, there is a tremendous amount that is unknown when it comes to screening out genetic defects.

A professor, Dr Helmuth Wachtel, wrote to me, saying that I was totally wrong about the vaccine issue. It's all down to faulty breeding, he told me. He explained how animals in the wild choose their own mates, whereas humans choose the mates for their breeding stock. The significance of this was demonstrated in a TV programme recently, which asked why beautiful young women so commonly married elderly rich men. An experiment in the programme entailed a beautiful young woman sniffing the sweat-stained towels of men who had been working out in the gym. Going only on scent, the woman decided that (unknown to her) she had favoured the plug-ugliest man in the gym. The commentator explained that we use our sense of smell to choose individuals who are least similar to us in genetic traits. (The elderly rich choice probably had more to do with the word 'rich'.) This whole concept turns the animal breeding programme on its head.

I had my own demonstration of a dog choosing the most appropriate mate several years earlier. Gwinnie was in season and rejected the young apparently virile, and very handsome, Samson, in favour of Chappie who was at that time 13 years old. Although I didn't know it at the time, Gwinnie did: Samson had cancer. Maybe the Viennese professor has a point.

A retired vet seems to have some simple but sensible ideas with regard to breeding out genetic defects in dogs. His organisation, called BRACE (Breeding Resistance Against Cancer Etc), was established in 1994 with the aim of breeding out cancer in dogs.

Dr Macadam's view was that any individual dog having malignant cancer, confirmed by a pathologist, should not produce further offspring. He also advocated accentuating the positive by breeding more from those families which have resistance to cancer. By breeding for longevity, he argued, we will breed out cancer. He therefore favoured the use of the oldest stud dog possible, reasoning that if he had reached a good age without a terminal illness, then he was likely to be genetically sound.

"If we have a choice between two equally good dogs, both winners at Crufts, one being two and the other ten, I would use the older dog," Macadam wrote. "He is a survivor, therefore he has the genes for longevity. He has no cancer, nor heart defect, nor diabetes. He is still sound in wind and limb, of excellent disposition and character. Thus we avoid cancer in the next generation. What of the two year old? We pray for the best, but we cannot guarantee his future. By the time he is six, he may be dying of cancer, heart problems, or have diabetes. Why would I take a chance of using him?" Dr Macadam's charity, BRACE, had the following objectives:

1.   To breed more offspring from any individuals from families with little or no history of cancer.

2. To avoid further offspring from any individual having cancer.

Criteria for success included:

1. Early diagnosis. Any lump, swelling of the abdomen or loss of weight should be investigated.
2. Diagnosis of cancer should be confirmed by a pathologist.
3. After confirmation of cancer a bitch must not be used for breeding. Dogs should be neutered.
4. Stud dogs should be free from cancer, heart problems, diabetes and mental problems. They should be sound in wind and limb, with good eyesight, hearing and excellent temperament.
5. Where two dogs are equally good the oldest stud dog should be favoured as guaranteeing the genes for more resistance to cancer.
6. Dogs aged eight or older should be shown so that other breeders can see what is on offer as potential stud dogs.
7. The date of birth should be included after the name of each dog and under each photograph.
8. Avoid the breeding of any dog known to carry genes for any inherited diseases, such as Progressive Retinal Atrophy or Familial Nephropathy.
9. Rather than pick Best of Breed we might do better to pick Top Ten Best of Breed. This would take the pressure off the individual and leave it to owners of bitches to decide which if any of these Top Ten to use.

But, then, I ask myself: what is the point of screening-out genetic defects if we are potentially introducing them by feeding inappropriately and vaccinating our animals? Isn't this just fire fighting? As stated previously, Dr Larry Glickman does not believe that we can necessarily say that autoantibodies found in his study automatically lead to autoimmune disease. But the sponsors of the study have indicated that it's possible.

Dr William R La Rosa MD, Trustee of the Hayward Foundation which funded the Purdue study, is dedicated to research to eradicate human genetic diseases. Dr La Rosa wrote, 'When the dog vaccine safety issue was brought to our attention by Laura Kiaulenas, a prominent Great Dane Breeder, and after reading articles by Jean

Dodds DVM, we decided to fund a study to prove or disprove the supposition of multiple diseases, acute and chronic, caused by vaccination. If indeed, many breeders are correct, then is the dog a canary sentinel, and are humans similarly being affected, and if so can we identify the dog or human who is genetically susceptible to these reactions?

'We were fortunate that prominent and respected researchers, Drs. Larry T. Glickman, Harm HogenEsch, Juan I. Azona-Olivera, J. Catherine Scott-Montcrieff, and Paul W. Snyder of Purdue University, School of Veterinary Medicine, agreed to undertake the study.

'Their study was based on the increasing concern among veterinarians and breeders that current vaccination protocols adversely affect the health of dogs. This concern has largely been based on anecdotal and circumstantial evidence. They studied the effects of routinely used vaccination protocol on the immune and endocrine systems of Beagles. One control group was not vaccinated and the other group was vaccinated with a commercial multivalent vaccine at 8, 10, 12, 16, and 20 weeks of age and with a rabies vaccine at 16 weeks of age.

'A definition of autoimmune disease is now necessary. In dogs as well as humans, the body sometimes forms antibodies against itself (self antigens) which can lead to diseases of the pancreas (diabetes), thyroid (Hashimoto's Disease), collagen and fibronectin (Scleroderma, Lupus), cardiolipin (Cardiomyopathy), etc. The body literally attacks itself to cause the autoimmune disease.

'The vaccinated group developed significant levels of autoantibodies against: fibronectin, laminin, albumin, Cytochrome C, transferrin, DNA, cardiolipin and collagen. The responses varied among individual animals, probably reflecting genetic differences. The clinical significance of those autoantibodies remains to be determined, but speculation must be that something in the vaccines is one of the etiologies (in the genetically susceptible dog) of such diseases as Cardiomyopathy, Lupus Erythematosus, Glomerulo-nephritis, etc.

'Autoimmune diseases are quite common in dogs as well as in humans, but much easier to study in dogs, especially since various breeds have genetic susceptibility or predisposition. The high prevalence of autoimmune disease in specific breeds makes it easier to search for the genetic markers. Humans are much more diverse and therefore more difficult to study. We hope that many Breed Associations and the AKC Foundation will join us in expanding these studies with the needed research funds. Longer term studies are needed to determine the clinical importance of vaccine-induced autoantibodies and to identify markers of genetic susceptibility.

'These are truly remarkable results. The next step is to study the development of safer vaccines, or possibly modify the recommended dosages, and the timing of vaccinations. Many vaccines, including a vaccine for use in humans, contain fibronectin. This appears to be a common contaminant. Other antigens will be studied.

'A general theme of the Conference was that vaccine immunity lasts longer than the manufacturer claims; rabies is probably effective for at least 3 years and we are probably over-vaccinating our dogs. Even the vaccine industry tells you that there is never 100% protection. Therefore disease is seen even in vaccinated groups. In Europe, vaccines are prohibited once the disease is eliminated because the fear of reversion to virulence of the modified live virus.

'Autoimmune diseases in dogs are clinically similar to those in humans. We hope that Veterinary and Medical Schools will continue and expand these preliminary research studies. Our companion dogs are crashing all around us and maybe we are now finding one of the sources of the problems. It has been so easy to point fingers at breeders but they may not be entirely at fault. Let us continue this important research to help our future generations of dogs and possibly children. Yes, indiscriminate breeding can genetically predispose the dog but is the trigger mechanism indiscriminate vaccinations?'

Notice that Dr La Rosa didn't suggest that, following this research into Beagles, we try to find out which humans carry faulty genes and eradicate them from the breeding programme. He said, 'The next step is to study the development of safer vaccines, or possibly modify the recommended dosages, and the timing of vaccinations. Many vaccines, including a vaccine for use in humans, contain fibronectin. This appears to be a common contaminant. Other antigens will be studied.'

Other research is worth looking at. Between 1996 and 1998, the Leading Edge Research Group presented data indicating that vaccines produce negative genetic changes in humans. Their report states:

'One of the indications that vaccinations may in fact be changing the genetic structure of humans became evident in September of 1971, when scientists at the University of Geneva made the discovery that biological substances entering directly into the bloodstream could become part of human genetic structure. Originally, Japanese bacteriologists discovered that bacteria of one species transferred their own specific antibiotic resistance to bacteria of an entirely different species. Dr. Maurice Stroun and Dr. Philip Anker in the Department of Plant Physiology at the University of Geneva, began to accumulate evidence that the transfer of genetic information is not confined to bacteria, but can also occur between bacteria and higher plants and animals.

'According to an article in *World Medicine* on September 22, 1971,Geneva scientists are convinced that normal animal and plant cells shed DNA, and that this DNA is taken up by other cells in the organism.

'There is evidence that freely circulating foreign DNA can cause malignancy. The discovery in 1975 that viruses causing cancer in animals had a special enzyme called *reverse transcriptase* makes the problem even more interesting. These kind of viruses are called RNA viruses. When an RNA virus has the reverse transcriptase enzyme within its structure, it allows the virus to actually form strands of DNA which easily integrate with the DNA of the host cell which it infects.

'Studies by Dr. Robert Simpson of Rutgers University indicate that RNA viruses which do not cause cancer can also form DNA, even without the presence of reverse transcriptase. DNA formed in this way from an RNA virus is called a *provirus*. It is known that some non-cancerous viruses have a tendency to exist as proviruses for long periods of time in cells without causing any apparent disease. In other words, they remain latent.

'Some examples of common RNA viruses that do not cause cancer, per se, but have the capacity to form proviruses are influenza, measles (distemper), mumps and polio viruses.

'In the October 22, 1967 *British Medical Journal*, it was stated by German scientists that multiple sclerosis seemed to be provoked by vaccinations against smallpox, typhoid, tetanus, polio, tuberculosis and diptheria. Even earlier, in 1965, Zintchenko reported 12 cases in which MS became evident after a course of anti-rabies vaccinations.

172

'Remember that millions of people between 1950 and 1970 were injected with polio vaccines containing simian virus 40 (SV-40) transferred from contaminated monkey kidney cells used to culture the vaccine. *It is impossible to remove animal viruses from vaccine cultures.* You are reminded that SV-40, the 40th virus to be discovered in simian tissue, is a cancer-causing virus.

'Immunization programs against influenza, measles, mumps and polio are in fact seeding humans with RNA and forming proviruses which become latent for long periods in throughout the body, only to re-awaken later on.

'Post-polio syndrome is a good example of this problem. Other examples may include the so-called mesenchymal and collagen diseases, such as rheumatoid arthritis, multiple sclerosis and lupus erythmatosis, where antibodies are formed by the immune system against the person's own tissues - tissues which have been impregnated with foreign genetic material. According to a special issue of *Postgraduate Medicine* in May 1962, *"although the body generally will not make antibodies against its own tissues, it appears that slight modification of the antigenic character of tissues may cause it to appear foreign to the immune system and thus a fair target for antibody production."*

'Even common non-tumour viruses, including those in smallpox vaccine and polio virus 2, can act as carcinogens. It was reported in *Science* on December 15, 1961 that these common viruses acted as catalysts in producing cancer when given to mice in combination with known organic carcinogens in amounts too small to induce tumours themselves. This means that some vaccinations will induce cancer, when combined with the growing problem of environmental pollution from toxic by-products of agriculture (pesticides on and in food) and industry.

'The use of viruses, bacteria and animal tissue cultures in mass immunization campaigns, considering that this information has been known for 20 years, constitutes an intentionally created hazard to humans. The global impact on the wide range of genotypes relative to human beings is difficult to assess, but the outcome is definitely negative, and permitting the seeding of latent proviruses in humans, knowingly, can have no other rationale other than future medical profiteering, and constitutes a criminal conspiracy of vast proportions which is tantamount to a genocidal policy against the population,

173

further constituting crimes against humanity, which is internationally punishable by death. But, of course, especially in the United States, this fact is ignored and suppressed from public knowledge, despite a 1984 plea by some U.S. physicians to the United Nations in a report.

'Persistence of long-term viruses and foreign proteins and their relationship to chronic and degenerative disease was also pointed out by Dr. Robert Simpson of Rutgers University in 1976, when he addressed science writers at an American Cancer Society seminar, saying *"these proviruses could be molecules in search of a disease."* Dr. Wendell Winters, a virologist at the University of California noted, *"immunizations may cause changes in slow viruses and changes in the DNA mechanism'.*

Added to this, Gary Smith's new theory on the inflammatory process is extremely important. When we introduce vaccines into the body, we are simply allowing the viruses to hide within the inflammation and spread their unwanted effects under the cover of darkness. If I were a science fiction writer, I'd be writing a book about viruses taking over the planet.

Rather than halt the effects of viral disease, vaccines appear to be helping the viruses to replicate, and to thrive as parasites in human and animal bodies – sucking the lifeblood out of us. But this is my interpretation. You are of course free to make your own, or to explain why I am wrong.

One thing we do know, however: in their data sheets, a number of veterinary vaccine manufacturers warn that an animal's immune system may be faulty due to a number of factors, including their genes. It is logical to assume that, if the animal's genetic makeup renders his immune system faulty, then he might not be able to deal with the vaccine challenge (or the viruses we vaccinate against). Some breeds of dogs, for example, are known for their lack of response to vaccines, and their inability to acquire immunity.

Vaccines, or genes, or food – what is the answer?

We are all of us genetically defective in some way. In human families, some are predisposed to cancer, others to allergies, others to nervous conditions, and others to specific genetically-inherited diseases such a sickle cell anaemia. The same applies to the animal world.

We tend to believe that we cannot change what we are physically born with, our genes – although scientists are currently working at DNA level in an attempt to physically alter genetic faults. My view is that we absolutely can change what we are born with by reprogramming our beliefs about what is possible.

Dogs are genetically predisposed to get run over by cars; the simple solution is to avoid having them play on the road. There are all sorts of things we can do to make sure that our genetic faults are expressed, and there are all sorts of things we can do to make sure they are not.

If you take a look at your family members and the illnesses they suffer, it's easy to see what your own genetic weaknesses might be.

My own family is a prime example: all of us tend to suffer from inflammatory or allergic conditions. My sister Leslie has asthma; my sister Mollie and her daughter Rebecca have a skin condition that makes them itch, which my father also had. My brother Fred has hayfever. My great niece Katie is allergic to eggs. My mother had eczema and respiratory problems. I used to have hayfever, and was at one time allergic to cats, and I once had eczema. These are all inflammatory conditions, but I don't, reassuringly, know of one case of cancer in my family.

Inflammatory conditions are associated with B and T cell immunodeficiencies which, simplistically, means an unruly immune system. These are also considered to be hereditary, although T cell immunodeficiencies can be triggered by vaccines, as an example. I know that if people in my family want to avoid triggering any of their genetic predispositions, then subjecting themselves to vaccines isn't a good idea. Merck, as I've mentioned previously, tells us so. We shouldn't be vaccinated, due to our genes.

However, I grew out of my cat allergy. I cured my hayfever using a healing technique called Emotional Freedom Technique. I got rid of my eczema using nutritional therapy. We can do the same for the animals, so long as the people in power refrain from legislating away our ability to do so. Vets could also do it, but conventional vets are trained to treat symptoms, rather than cause, and to distrust any healing modality that isn't supported by the trials few but the pharmaceutical industry can afford to conduct.

It's interesting to see that schizophrenia, thought to have a genetic basis, has been treated with folic acid and B6, or folic acid alone, at high potencies. Others respond to vitamin B3 plus vitamin C. Occasionally, vitamin B12 injections have helped.

Cancer is another disease in which nutrients can be used therapeutically – to both prevent and treat. We have all heard of the women who, knowing that breast cancer is common in their families (a genetic predisposition), have chosen to have their breasts removed rather than wait for the potential event. However, research has shown that people living in selenium-deficient areas have a higher rate of cancer than those living in areas where there are high selenium levels.

Selenium is irregularly distributed in soils of various countries, and in areas within the same country. This is reflected in the selenium content of the food grown in those areas. Selenium intake is lower, for example, in the USA than in Bulgaria, and cancer rates are also lower in Bulgaria. Within Bulgaria itself, those with higher blood selenium levels have a lower incidence of cancer than those with low blood selenium levels.

The functions of selenium include maintaining resistance to disease, protecting against toxic minerals, acting as an anti-inflammatory agent, maintaining a healthy heart, and acting as an anti-oxidant. Experiments have proven that some cancers can actually be cured with selenium supplementation.

Vitamins C and E have also been shown to have preventative and therapeutic effects on cancer. Vitamin C is found in many fruits and vegetables. It acts as an anti-oxidant, maintains healthy collagen, provides resistance to infection, produces anti-stress hormones; produces brain and nerve substances, and makes folic acid active. Folic acid, itself, is needed for the metabolism of RNA and DNA, and genetic code transmission, and can be used therapeutically in the treatment of schizophrenia, psychosis, mental deterioration and certain forms of anaemia.

Eating food with folic acid when pregnant can greatly reduce the incidence of spina bifida and other birth defects, including neural tube defects. So, a deficiency in vitamin C and/or folic acid, could lead to apparent genetic defects. The words chicken and egg come to mind.

Vitamin E, amongst other things, prevents thrombosis and promotes the ability of white blood cells to resist infection. It is used by athletes and in racehorses to increase endurance and stamina. Positive clinical responses have been obtained for breast cancer conditions by using 200IU vitamin E three times daily and up to 10g of vitamin C daily.

The question, therefore, is how much of cancer is an hereditary condition, and how much is it to do with the geographical location of the family, and the eating habits of a family? How much of it is related to what your forebears ate? I'm just asking the questions here.

Susan Donoghue, a vet and nutritionist, wrote an interesting paper about one of her patients, Ollie, who suffered from a genetically-based copper storage disease. Susan explained that genetics affect dietary requirements: some dogs (individuals or breeds) may have higher needs for specific nutrients. She wrote, 'We usually feed the phenotype, the dog we see. But sometimes we need to think about the dog hidden within, the genotype that may interact with nutrition in three ways. First, genetic differences between individuals affect requirements for energy and nutrients. Second, nutrition may affect dogs that are genetically susceptible to certain disorders. Third, there are genetic defects that block pathways involving nutrients or their by-products.

'Certain breeds of dogs tend to have increased susceptibility to specific diseases. Clearly, not every dog at risk for a disease actually develops the problem. Other factors in the environment probably play a role in the development of disease, and sometimes nutrition might influence this process.'

Ollie, Dr Donoghue explained, had been treated for ten years with a drug (penicillamine) that binds copper so that less copper is available to the body. However, the drug also binds zinc, and after ten years, Ollie developed the classic signs of zinc deficiency, namely reddened skin around the eyes and between the toes, poor appetite, and small testicles. He also received medical treatment for hepatitis. In six months of zinc therapy (which binds copper with fewer side-effects than penicillamine), Ollie was a new dog with a bounce in his step, a decent appetite, and a luxuriant coat. Ollie lived several more years. Dr Donoghue concluded that Ollie had helped her to understand the potential of using homemade diets to manage specific genetic disorders.

Hip dysplasia in dogs is also thought to be a genetic condition. However, the vet Wendell Belfield discovered that HD is remarkably similar to one of the symptoms of scurvy in humans. He experimented with vitamin C therapy, giving high doses of the vitamin to dogs who were apparently genetically predisposed to hip dysplasia. None of the dogs developed the alleged genetic condition. Meanwhile, breeders continue to have breeding stock x-rayed and hip scored in an attempt to eradicate HD. This method doesn't seem to be working, since the parents' hip scores seem to have only a tenuous correlation to the scores of their progeny. Where HD is concerned, eugenics isn't *apparently* working, but vitamin therapy has been shown to work.

Dr Belfield also believes that lameness, arthritis, spinal myelopathy, ruptured disc, skin problems and Vital disease are symptoms of vitamin C deficiency, and there is some good research to support his view.

So my point is this: We need to take an holistic view of health. We need to synthesize the bodies we inherit with the food we eat, and with a better understanding of what we can do to mitigate and prevent the expression of disease.

I don't believe it is necessary to vaccinate against disease. I believe it is possible to live in the world in such a way that our immune systems combat disease challenge. We can do this with knowledge of nutrients, and by changing the way we all look at the world.

Ten
Stress

Over the years, looking at the reasons for ill health in our dogs, it has become increasingly clear to me that 'stress' is perhaps the greatest cause of disease in both man and domestic animals. We live with disease all the time; many pathogens already exist in the body. Illness starts in the mind; we choose to be healthy. I've wondered why, believing in a benevolent creation, we should have viruses and bacterins that make vaccines necessary. My conclusion is that pathogens simply act as helpers should we decide it is time to leave. Vaccines, containing viruses and bacterins, do the same, but in a different way.

As many vaccine data sheets state, an animal's immune system may be compromised by stress, which can hinder their ability to handle a vaccine challenge. We are more susceptible to disease when we are under stress, but we are also more susceptible to an adverse vaccine reaction when we are under stress, because stress compromises the immune system's ability to operate effectively. The body, in fact, mirrors the mind's decision when it's time to go.

It appears that vaccine manufacturers, in their data sheets, are saying that animals might not develop immunity from the vaccine if they are vaccinated when under stress. It is possible, though, that individuals might also have an unwanted or damaging reaction to the vaccine if they are vaccinated while stressed. It's this possibility that I want to explore here.

A number of studies were designed by Ronald Glaser PhD from the department of medical microbiology and immunology, Behaviour Medicine Research Institute at Ohio State University, in order to explore the impact of different kinds of psychological stressors on the immune response. In one study, 48 medical students were inoculated with a series of Hepatitis B vaccines to coincide with the third day of a three day exam series. Hep-B specific antibody levels and Hep-B specific T-cell responses were measured. Students who reported greater social support and lower anxiety and stress had higher antibody levels to the vaccine and a more vigorous T-cell response at the end of the third inoculation.

In a second series of studies, caregivers of Alzheimers patients were given the influenza virus vaccine, and they were shown to have impaired cellular immune responses when compared to control subjects.

The differences in antibody and T-cell responses to these two viruses demonstrated how psychological stress may be able to alter a person's response to a vaccine and therefore risk for infection. Dr Glaser commented that, 'We believe that data obtained with these two vaccines provide a clue for how stress can affect how a person would respond to infection with a live virus.'

Dr Glaser points towards an important question: why do some people withstand viral challenge unscathed, and why do some people withstand a vaccine challenge unscathed? Why do some dogs, cats and horses appear to withstand over-vaccination without apparent harm, while others seem to have adverse reactions? Does the answer lie in the level of stress in their lives?

There is, of course, a genetic component in all of this – but not all individuals from a family will react in the same way to a vaccine challenge. Our inter-bred dogs are a good example of this, because if all dogs in a line suffered adverse vaccine reactions, it would be fairly obvious and one would hope that this book would be unnecessary.

Ohio State University also studied how well a pneumonia vaccination will protect elderly people depending on how stressed they are when they get the shots. The study, reported in the journal of *Psychosomatic Medicine*, showed that even after six months, the vaccine may have been weakened by a person's stress levels. Dr Glaser advised that if you're highly stressed when you are scheduled for shots, maybe you should reschedule. The pneumonia vaccine study followed similar studies such as the influenza vaccines and Hepatitis-B vaccine studies mentioned above, and another on the rubella virus, the causative agent in measles. In all of these experiments, high stress levels had a negative impact on the efficacy of the vaccines.

Among other indicators, the researchers were interested in the levels of immunoglobin-G (IgG), an antibody formed by the body to fend off pneumococcal bacteria. Strong IgG levels indicated a healthy immune response ready to protect against the disease while weaker levels mean that a person could be at risk from pneumonia.

When they analysed the data, they found that all three groups - current caregivers, former caregivers and members of the control group - showed an initial positive response to the vaccine. But after six months, the immune status of the current caregivers dropped precipitously while controls and former caregivers remained the same. With the bacterial vaccine, the effect arose only later, showing up at the three-month and six-month blood tests. Glaser suggests two possible explanations:

Viral infections - like influenza - cause the body to do two things. First, antibodies specifically targeted against the virus are produced and flood the bloodstream. And second, the body produces killer T-lymphocytes that can identify cells infected by the virus and kill them.

But with bacterial infections - like pneumonia - the killer T-lymphocytes are not as important. Instead, B-lymphocytes, which make the specific antibodies to the bacteria, are the key. They work with the T-lymphocytes to fight the infection. 'Perhaps the stress causes a reduction in the total number of B-lymphocytes the body produces over time and so there are less cells making the antibody needed for the immune response,' he posed. Or maybe there are enough B-lymphocytes but they make less of the antibodies.

'At this point, we just don't know.'

This research shows that the immune response of an individual who is under stress is not as good as the response of a lesser stressed individual. It occurs to me that vaccine manufacturers, knowing this, may have historically advocated annual revaccination, hoping to provide cover next year for the ones who didn't respond this year. It may also be one of the reasons why professional bodies such as the BSAVA continue to advocate annual shots.

Unfortunately, it may also be that stressed individuals not only fail to develop adequate immunity from vaccines, but that they are more likely to develop an adverse reaction, and so the more shots they are given, the more chance there is of causing damage.

Stress defined

Stress is defined for humans by the British Health and Safety Executive (HSE) as 'the adverse reaction people have to excessive pressures or other types of demand placed on them'. The HSE distinguishes between the beneficial effects of reasonable pressure and challenge (which can be stimulating and motivating), and the natural but distressing reaction to demands or pressures that a person feels they cannot cope with.

You may be suffering from stress if you have aches and pains in your body, such as back pains, sore shoulders, and gastrointestinal disturbances. Stress is a known contributor to heart disease, and psychological effects include anxiety and depression. People with inflammatory conditions often find their conditions getting worse under times of stress: asthma will flare up, as will skin problems and other 'itis' (inflammatory) conditions such as arthritis.

The connection between emotions and the immune system

Research carried out by the Association for Research into the Science of Enjoyment has shown that happy thoughts and pleasant smells can boost the immune system. A study by Professor Warburton at Reading University in England showed that within 20 minutes of happy thoughts being experienced, the amount of antibody immunoglobulin (sIgA) found in the saliva doubled, remaining raised for at least three hours. By contrast, memory of traumatic or painful experiences caused the sIgA levels to drop.

Another study carried out by Angela Clow at the University of Westminster showed a similar response to unpleasant and pleasant smells (which is good news for aromatherapists).

Professor David Warburton said, 'Previous scientific experiments have observed a correlation between changing moods and the immune system, but these new studies provide a direct causal link. Identifying this direct link proves that happiness could make you healthier.'

The science of psychoneuroimmunology shows how emotions and the immune system are totally connected with one-another. As this science increasingly demonstrates, what we think affects what we feel (our emotions), and what we feel affects our physical bodies. I suspect that one day research will be conducted to demonstrate that animals suffering from immune-mediated diseases are more often than not living in homes where the humans are suffering from high levels of stress, and especially where there is a strong bond between the stressed human and their animal.

Psychoneuroimmunology shows us that when we are happy, our bodies produce the hormone *serotonin*, which increases *physical and emotional* wellbeing. Indeed, scientific studies have shown that we are less susceptible to colds and flu when we are happy - because happiness helps the immune system to function. Conversely, we are more susceptible to viruses and other illnesses when we are under stress.

Psychoneuroimmunologists have found that stimulatory signals focus in the stressed body upon the paraventricular nucleus (PVN) in the hypothalamus. The central neurotransmitters involved in activation are monoamines, which include serotonin. Cells in the PVN also produce a peptide called corticotrophin releasing factor (CRF). CRF stimulates the release of the pituitary hormone adrenocorticotrophin (ACTH). This arrives at the adrenal cortex to stimulate the production of corticosteroids, notably cortisol. CRF therefore lies at the heart of the stress response. Interesting, too, that corticosteroids are inhibited by stress. They are used to help us, and our animals, to recover from inflammatory conditions which themselves, it now seems, may be how outside influences, whether they be emotional or mental stresses, vaccines, or viral and bacterial invaders, inhibit our ability to defend ourselves. This fact also offers an additional insight to Gary Smith's theory regarding the inflammatory response.

Importantly, not only is CRF released to stimulate the pituitary, it acts as a central neurotransmitter to influence mood and emotion and emotion-related behaviours. Among the target cells that respond to activity in this circuitry are cells of the immune system. In short, if your mind is under stress, your body is also under stress, and this can make you ill. It's all connected.

It seems to me that science and metaphysics are meeting at this point. The spiritual maxim has always been to attain equilibrium, sometimes expressed as tranquillity, or balance. Spiritual disciplines have long-focussed on the need to remain calm and at peace, which is why meditation is a central practice in most religions. Studies have also shown that meditation is good for your physical health.

From a holistic perspective, whilst bringing in data from conventional science, it appears that inflammation (maybe otherwise expressed as disruption) in our emotional, mental, physical or spiritual bodies can lead to disease. Going back to Hans Selye's non-specific response to stress, we see that stress causes all of the systems in the body to mobilise and, should the stress prove too great, the individual will die. Stress, in fact, is a shock to the system.

The nutrients we put in our bodies also determine whether we are able to mount a successful response to stress. If we get upset or stressed, the body will draw upon its stores of zinc, vitamin B5 and vitamin C, amongst others: these nutrients will become depleted. Conversely, when you are upset and stressed, you need these nutrients to feed anti-stress hormones. They are anti-stress nutrients, used by the immune system to fight the challenges your body and your emotions are facing. Vitamin C, for example, has been described as Nature's anti-histamine. It plays a vital role in reducing inflammation (disruption) in the body. This fact, incidentally, is why vitamin C supplementation may be necessary in some dogs, despite the fact that dogs manufacture their own vitamin C.

Wherever you look, whether it be at the conventional or holistic sciences; whether it's the study of nutrients or sports or even religion, the injunction of 'balance' is always present. The earth and all who inhabit her are always looking for balance: moderation in all things.

How our stress affects others

My observations lead me to conclude that the disease states caused by stress in humans can also be transferred to the animals and children in our care. Homoeopaths have long recognised that, for example, if you treat a mother in a family, the children's illnesses have a tendency to resolve. I guess the best way to justify this claim is to draw upon quantum physics which tells us that matter (the physical) is energy before it becomes matter. Our emotions are energies: emotions are our thoughts as they are experienced by the body. Emotions that are pleasant to the body include joy, laughter and love. Emotions that disrupt our bodies include anger, sorrow and fear.

Children and animals have fewer mechanisms with which they can defend themselves from our emotional energies – just as it takes years for the protective sheath called myelin to encapsulate the nerves in our body, it also takes years for humans to develop energetic or mental boundaries between themselves and others. I would think that almost all dog owners will be able to resonate with the statement that their dogs can pick up how they are feeling, and will often act out how they are feeling. I certainly know that if I am agitated, my dogs will become agitated; if I am calm, my dogs have a tendency to be calm.

There have been several studies on the effect of stress in children, and it is my contention that what happens to a child in a family as a result of stress can also happen to companion animals.

Mark Flinn from the University of Missouri has been studying the relationship between stress and health in children. He maintains that two of the best ways to measure stress are by asking questions and by measuring the adrenal hormone cortisol in saliva. Since 1998, Flinn has collected more than 25,000 saliva samples from 287 children in the same rural village on a Caribbean island for an average of 96 samples per child.

He has tracked the children's growth, measured their immunoglobulin levels to see if their immune systems are healthy, checked their health records and sent an assistant to visit the sick. Importantly, he has watched, listened and asked questions in order to really understand what is happening in their lives. Flinn has concluded that:

- Family matters more than anything else in a child's life.
- When a family has problems, it sends stress hormones coursing through a child's system.
- When family members get on well, or have numerous relatives to call on, they can shelter a child from the worst social upheavals in the outside world. Emotionally and physiologically, family life is paramount in a child's health.
- Illness among children increases more than twofold following significant stress.

The reason for this lies in a complex biological process. When a person is in trouble, the brain automatically sends signals to the sympathetic nervous system initiating a fight or flight response. This response may be summed up as follows:

- Lungs pump faster and the heart starts to race.
- Blood pressure rises, charging up the muscles and sharpening the mind.
- The stomach gets jumpy and the rush of endorphins numbs the body.
- The appetite, libido and immune system shut down, and the energy they would normally consume is diverted to muscles that will help the body fight the immediate threat.

185

This response is fine unless the perceived threat persists. In this case, adrenaline washes out of the body quickly, but cortisol may linger for days, weeks or even years, keeping the immune system and other important functions depressed. Children are especially vulnerable to stress according to research at Stanford University. Long term, too much cortisol can slow down a child's growth, brain development and sexual maturity. In the short term, it can make a child prone to infections.

According to Flinn, there is nothing more important to a child than working out what makes those close to them happy, and what makes them sad. He found that children who live with both biological parents clearly do best. They have lower average cortisol levels, weigh more, and grow more steadily than those living with stepparents or single parents with no support from relatives. He also found that chronically high cortisol levels in children are very dangerous because it can cause permanent damage.

The children studied in this trial inhabited a tranquil island that wasn't affected by the rat race. There were no traffic stresses, no inner city problems. The stresses were normal family stresses – possibly of a lower severity than those faced by most people reading this book.

I would also add that even if dogs can't understand language or the implications of upsets, they certainly recognise anger and aggression, and will respond with the fight or flight response.

The consequences of extreme stress

The consequences of extreme stress are known to last for years. In Romania, orphans raised under the dictatorship of Ceausescu were so completely neglected that they became withdrawn and temperamental, and were prone to rocking in place and staring blankly at visitors. Psychologist Elinor Ames, of Simon Fraser University in British Columbia, studied two groups of these Romanian orphans. She found that many of those who were adopted by Americans but who had spent the longest time in the orphanage continued to suffer from depression and withdrawal.

It is also known that people who survive natural disasters or severe violence are at high risk for suffering years of post-traumatic stress disorder. In 1988, for example, thousands of Armenians were devastated by a severe earthquake; in that same year, political violence erupted against ethnic Armenians in neighbouring Azerbaijan. In a study of 78 Armenians who experienced either of these traumas, researchers found that both groups had similar, long-term symptoms of post-traumatic stress.

First widely recognised in veterans of the Vietnam War, post-traumatic stress disorder is now known to be a problem in the larger population. Anyone who survives intensely traumatic circumstances may show its signs and symptoms - including withdrawal from others, flashbacks, and feelings of helplessness.

The researchers looked at post-traumatic stress in three groups of adults whom they had first studied three years earlier. In one group, subjects had experienced minor earthquake damage, but were exposed to graphic depictions of destruction in other parts of the country. In another group, people had their lives directly threatened by the earthquake and had witnessed the death and destruction it caused. Subjects in the third group had experienced persecution in Azerbaijan, suffering threats to their own lives and witnessing the torture or murder of family or friends.

The investigators found that people in the two most seriously traumatized groups had the same level of post-traumatic stress symptoms. Moreover, time did nothing to abate symptoms in either group. On the other hand, depression in these groups had faded. The group that had experienced mild earthquake damage saw their post-traumatic stress symptoms ease.

The persistence of post-traumatic stress in the other two groups mirrors findings from studies of World War II prisoners-of-war and Cambodian refugees. Individuals in the Armenian study were surrounded by pervasive trauma reminders such as destroyed buildings, 'shoddy' homes, and media reports of violence in Azerbaijan. In addition, the post-traumatic stress had spurred other emotionally draining problems, such as difficulties at work and in marriage (*American Journal of Psychiatry* June 2000;157:911-916).

I think that people who experienced extreme abuse as children will have many of the symptoms of post-traumatic stress, to greater or lesser degree.

Recognising stress

Stress for the average person is essentially the state you get into because of the way you react to influences that you feel are outside of your control – such as money worries, relationship problems, the pressures of work, the death of a loved-one, the loss of a job, moving home, retirement, illness of a family member (which includes the animals), divorce, and feeling that there isn't enough time.

Many of the above stresses are the normal life events that we all have to face at some time or another. However, when we are constantly bombarded with these outside pressures over a prolonged period of time, and can't find a way to cope with them, illness can be the result.

Psychologists know that people respond to stressful situations in different ways. Everyone has different stress thresholds. Someone with a low stress threshold can become highly stressed by simple events, such as being late for a meeting or forgetting their keys. But it would take something much more threatening, like failing an exam or moving house, to initiate the stress response in a person with a high stress threshold.

Scientists have identified a series of different factors that can influence an individual's vulnerability to stress. Your age and sex seem to effect your stress susceptibility, but the major deciding factor appears to be your personality type. Psychologists talk about two personality types when it comes to stress: A or B. People with Type A personalities are more likely to rush, be competitive and be perfectionists. They often attempt to do two or more things at once and feel guilty when they take time out to relax or do nothing, even if it's just for a couple of hours. Type B personalities, on the other hand, are people who can be described as 'laid back'. They are easy going, able to work at a reasonable pace and can relax without guilt.

Not surprisingly, Type A people are much more prone to stress than Type B people. Any minor event that disrupts their normal routine or gets in the way of their plans can upset a Type A person, while a Type B person is much more able to take the world in their stride. They tend to be more adaptive in their thinking and are better able to put things in perspective, thinking through how they are going to deal with a situation rather than just stressing over it as a Type A person would.

There are various theories about what forms our personalities. Professor Carey Cooper, a psychologist from the University of Manchester, believes that our early childhood is responsible for how we behave as adults. 'We learn our coping strategies in life from our parents. We identify particularly with parents, we see how they deal with situations and we model that kind of behaviour.'

However, others argue that it is our genes, not our environment, which determine our future personalities - particularly the aggressive side of our personalities. If this is the case, people with aggressive tendencies will have a genetic predisposition to suffer from stress-related illnesses during their lifetimes.

Another idea, still, comes from Professor Vivette Glover, a researcher at Imperial College of Science Technology and Medicine. She has been investigating how a baby in the womb can be affected by its mother's mental state. Initial studies have shown that if a mother is suffering from stress when she is pregnant, it can lead to an increased risk of emotional problems in the child.

I believe that all of these scenarios play a part in the stress response, and that all of them can be healed. If I am correct, and I shall seek to explain why in the next chapter, then it offers us a way in which we can optimise our own health and longevity, and the health and longevity of our animals – irrespective of vaccines.

Stress can be felt in the body. You can measure how stressed you feel by running a scan over your body. Where does it hurt; where are you carrying tension? Interestingly, most of us are out of touch with how our bodies feel. We might notice pain briefly, but usually we ignore the pain until it is so intense that it cannot be ignored and we resort to some type of drug. Much of this is due to the fact that we haven't been taught, as a society, to be body-conscious, and we especially haven't been taught how to alleviate these signs of stress before they develop into real problems.

When you are stressed you may experience many different feelings, including anxiety, fear, anger, frustration and depression. These feelings can feed on each other and can themselves produce physical symptoms - making you feel even worse. Extreme anxiety can cause giddiness, heart palpitations, headaches or stomach disorders. Many of these symptoms may make you feel so unwell that you then worry that you have some serious physical conditions such as heart disease or cancer - making you even more stressed.

When you are stressed you may behave differently. For example, you may become withdrawn, indecisive or inflexible. You may not be able to sleep properly. You may be irritable or tearful all the time. There may be a change in your sexual habits, and even if you were previously mild-mannered you may suddenly become verbally or physically aggressive. It's ironic, really, that people who are feeling the effects of stress tend to behave in ways that isolate them from others, and that most of us try to avoid or condemn difficult people – the very people who may need our help the most. The animals fulfil a vital function in this respect, don't they.

Our stress and its impact on our animals

Animals who are brought into a family form a bond with the individuals in that family. Dogs in particular are very much based in their emotional and physical bodies. Most dog lovers will recognise that when they 'tut', a sensitive dog will react, either by running towards them to help their human companion or, if the human is to be feared, by running away. Dogs understand sighs, tuts, swearing and noises of frustration, sorrow and anger. They also tune into our physical state.

One of my dogs, Samson, used to notice when I was working too hard at the computer. He would come and take my arm gently in his mouth, and walk me upstairs and push me onto the bed. Gwinnie notices when I am writing about a difficult subject which is causing an emotional response in my body. In these circumstances she will start to make noises and fuss around me until I take a break. Sophie used to bark gently to me at night as I sat mulling over the events of the day, while everyone else was sleeping. Eventually I noticed that she only barked when I was having negative thoughts. By listening to our animals, and observing, I think most of us will find that they are far more aware of us and our moods than science has yet concluded.

The biologist Dr Rupert Sheldrake is at the leading edge of research into the animal-human bond. He has conducted an incredible body of work to demonstrate what he calls the 'morphic field', which is a sort of telepathic communications network that connects animals and humans, as well as humans and humans, who are bonded together. The phenomenon explains why birds in flight change direction together, how you can think of a person a split second before the phone rings and it's them, and how dogs seem to know when their owners are coming home. Scientists have even demonstrated that cells, when separated – and placed in separate locations – maintain communications with one-another and act in tandem. We seem to be connected by a vast, all-embracive, communications network.

Dr Sheldrake has conducted hundreds of experiments, videoing dogs in outbuildings with their owners simply thinking about taking the dog for a walk at randomised times. Immediately the owner has the thought, the dogs start jumping up and down with excitement. Dr Sheldrake has also conducted experiments with parrots who have been taught a large vocabulary. In one example, he cites the parrot's owner having a dream about turning on a tape recorder, only to be woken by the parrot screaming 'press the button' in her ear. So much information is coming together to show that the mental powers of both humans and animals are not restricted to the physical activities in the brain, but that we are all connected to a 'unifying field of intelligence' that surrounds all living things. We are all connected.

My own experience using Emotional Freedom Technique – a healing technique similar to acupuncture but without the needles that treats the emotional root cause of illness – has shown in many instances that behaviour problems in companion animals can be alleviated or even removed by encouraging the owner to use the technique on their own emotional issues. One example is of a Cavalier King Charles Spaniel who was aggressive to other dogs. When the owner worked on her fear of her dog being attacked, the Spaniel's aggression disappeared. Similarly, when another lady used the technique to alleviate her own distrust of strangers, her dog stopped growling at approaching strangers in the park. Animals seem to mirror their owners.

Those who rescue dogs will also be able to relate to the excitable and uncontrollable dogs who, when taken from their previous excitable and uncontrolled owners, calm down very quickly in a more tranquil environment. Horse riders clearly know that horses respond to their own moods.

These examples demonstrate that our emotions (energies felt in the body, triggered by thoughts) can be picked up and carried by our animals. Similarly, children have been seen to 'act out' their parents' felt but unexpressed or stuffed emotions. I believe that the same is true of the animals.

Consequently, if an animal's closest human companion is suffering from stress – either current stress or as a result of traumatic events from the past – then the animal will at least be aware of his person's physiological and psychological condition. Indeed, dogs are being used to alert their owners to an impending epileptic fit and, in some cases, have been able to demonstrate a knowledge of the presence of cancer. It may not be too remarkable that both of these illnesses, cancer and epilepsy, are related to inflammation – which can also be described in quantum physics terms as an imbalance of energies.

Having now recognised the effects of stress on the immune system, what can we do about it?

Eleven
A radical approach to stress

My friend Julie is a lovely human being whose boyfriend Gary is also a lovely human being. Unfortunately, Julie and Gary have a lot of big arguments. Not long after a particularly big bust-up, Julie's dog Micki started to collapse whilst on walks, and the vet confirmed haemangeosarcoma, a fast-moving, blood-borne cancer. Micki's spleen was removed and she began to make a good recovery. Pretty soon she was off running on the beach again with Julie each morning. Then Julie and Gary had another big bust-up, and Micki took a turn for the worse. She was put to sleep a week after the big row. Julie believes, with conviction, that Micki was picking up on the stress in her relationship, and that this made her ill.

Of course, the prognosis for a dog with this type of cancer isn't great, although one homoeopathic vet did tell me that he had known dogs to recover from it. I wish, though, that I could have told Julie that I didn't think the arguments might be involved in Micki's illness, but I believe that similar stresses were involved in my own dogs' illnesses.

Like children, our animals are fairly defenceless when it comes to stress. They simply don't have the boundaries that humans develop as adults. When bad things happen around them, they are hurled into the flight or fight response, and there is only so much of this a sensitive individual can take. And animals are extremely sensitive to energies.

Robert Louis Stevenson wrote, 'There is no duty we so much underrate as the duty of being happy'. I believe that there is far more to this statement than Mr Stevenson might have imagined. By this I do not mean that we should put on a brave face and act as if we are happy. Neither do I believe that we should blame ourselves if, through our unhappiness, our animals suffer. Guilt is an emotion that is meant to come and go fairly quickly: it is there to tell us that some changes could be made, and that reparation might also be appropriate. It is not there for us to wear like a hair shirt – that would merely compound the problem.

Instead, I think we need to think seriously about a statement someone made to me many years ago: 'The animals have been concerned with human evolution since the beginning of time'. It is, I believe, their great joy to help us on our path.

'Emmanuel's Book', channelled by Pat Rodegast, contains many interesting concepts. On illness, Emmanuel said:

So much can be gathered
in that time of quietness, of introspection,
that illness forces upon you dear souls
who are always outer motivated.
Such times can be used
for the alchemy of taking the clay of physicality
and breathing the spirit into it
that will change that clay into gold.

Illness is a teaching,
a message from the soul.
When the lessons are learned
the illness becomes
a thing of no moment.

Illness is the confusion of that particular soul
manifesting physically
so that the consciousness will see it.

Every part of an illness is you.
Listen to your body.
What is it saying?
Be that part of your body.
Once you have heard the voice
of those areas that are recalcitrant,
the mature mind can say,
'Let's find another way.'
At that point, you quite literally
embrace the aberrated energy within you,
whether it is mental, physical or emotional,
and start to de-energise it
by simple acceptance of it.
The transformation begins.

Pain speaks to you
when you are ready to learn from it.

Emotional pain says one thing,
physical pain another.
Even its location in the body is eloquent.
Nothing in life happens haphazardly.
I realise that is a hard thing to hear
when someone is in pain
but the truth is the truth.
You live in a sane and ordered universe.
Make that your tenet.

Illness exists first in the non-physical realm
of spiritual need,
emotional confusion,
or mental aberration.
It is never primarily physical.
The body is the reactor.
It vibrates to stress
and is an outward manifestation
of inner turmoil.

As the body constricts
under the onslaught of trauma,
there is a denial of energy
to a particular part of the body.
Thus the stage is set
for a physical manifestation
which is, in your reality,
a malfunction of the body.

Illnesses are classified
by their symptomatic manifestation
but their causes can be totally different.
The same illness
may exist in two different entities
for two different reasons.
It is the way that each body
expresses
its outpicturing of disunity.

In the previous, chapter, we saw different theories as to why some people can handle stress better than others. One school of thought is that we are driven behaviourally by our genes. Another is that our early childhood is responsible for how we behave as adults. And a third is that babies in the womb are affected by their mothers' mental and emotional state.

We are not too different to the animals, you know. My partner Rob Ellis wrote the following piece for one of Canine Health Concern's newsletters, concerning the crucial first few weeks in a puppy's life:

Dogs have a period in their lives where their brain literally 'grows' and all that happens during this period will affect the rest of their lives. This can range from the tiniest event that, if not repeated, will be insignificant, right up to major events that will shape behaviour for life. After this, behaviour can be modified but we can all think of examples where it is difficult to modify or eradicate behaviour once it has been established, so the art is to ensure our dogs have been equipped to live in our world – the environment they are required to live in.

Of course all dogs are individuals and there are breed differences, but the principles remain the same. The socialisation window has a cut off point and is also linked to fear onsets and offsets, and a rough guide is that this window closes around the age of sixteen weeks.

I could write a book on problems that occur purely through incorrect or lack of socialisation in dogs, ranging from aggression (this also includes perceived aggression that is not always what we think) to difficulty with training and general behaviour throughout normal life. Actually, this is a major point – isn't all life normal?

Sure there are exceptional circumstances that occur, but training and living life is a process that is continuous, it doesn't stop just because we finish an obedience session. Life is one long experience and not split into training sessions and normal life. Training is only one part within life as a whole.

For example, there are many people whose dogs never get to mix with other dogs, say hello to them even, and we see it every day, people all walking separately and dogs never getting to mix with their own species – how awful is that? And what do we do? We blame the dog if something goes wrong. No dog is a bad dog, some dogs learn unsuitable or unwanted behaviour, simple as that.

There are obviously other factors involved like medical/ psychological disorders (in which case they need to be diagnosed and treated) but then it is all down to what he/she has been and is made to live like, including training. I like to term everything under the heading of 'life training'. That means her whole world – I cannot stress that enough: from a pup her whole world has to be given a number of weeks' total effort on the part of the owner, taking her places, meeting and seeing anyone and everyone, all in a positive way, handling, socialising with everything, training from the smallest of 'comes' through to all basic obedience.

Cars, buses, trains, vets, woods, beaches, stairs, noises, strange objects, anything and everything you can think of . . . TV, washing machines, hi-fi, fireworks, guns, thunder. Dogs of all sizes and colours and breeds, sheep, rabbits, cows, guinea pigs, cats, children and people of all shapes, sizes, gender, with beards, moustaches, hats, wooden legs, wheelchairs, all of it, everything possible.

There are of course the right ways to go about these events and in the right pace, but if it is all done in a gentle and positive manner then after your dog is sixteen weeks old (or thereabouts) he/she will have the equipment and experience to be the 'master of the universe', 'sound as a pound'.

There is more to deal with after that age but the imprinted information will live with him forever and if it is all good then with a good environment, proper *training, stimulation, exercise, motivation, correct diet and loads and loads of love – hey, how on earth could you have a dog that would be anything other than quite possibly the best dog in the world? And boy what a personality he would have.*

So there you have it. Humans aren't too different to dogs. I particularly like Rob's statement that, 'no dog is a bad dog; some learn unsuitable or unwanted behaviour, as simple as that'. It seems to me that human beings can also be judged in similarly charitable terms – even the people I disagree with!

Much of the literature I have seen counsels that you take up meditation, or listen to music, or allow yourself to have a massage to counteract stress . . . all of which are wonderful and beneficial things to do . . . but they don't, in my view, go deep enough quickly enough when it comes to alleviating the damaging effects of stress.

In order to truly combat stress at its source, we need to go within and reprogramme our early programming. We need, in effect, to throw out the unhelpful beliefs we have about ourselves and the world which, as happens to puppies, develop in the earliest stages of our lives. Meditation will, of course, do this for us – but I also wish to provide an understanding of the faulty programming that is driving us, and offer a faster way to reprogramme it. I appreciate that this is something that many people do not wish to do, and I also appreciate that you may not be expecting this information in a book about animal health. I offer it, anyway, in the hope that it is helpful to at least some of you, and that an understanding of the root of stress will help both you and your animals. I believe that if we can name something, then it ceases to have power over us.

In addition to loving and working with the animals, I have also worked all of my life to understand myself and other people. This has included being a practical student of philosophy, reading every spiritual text I could get my hands on, and learning Emotional Freedom Technique, which is a healing technique that addresses issues involving the emotions and the mind. I have had the privilege to teach this technique to hundreds of people, and to use it myself to heal myself.

In my life, I have met countless people who don't like themselves very much. A woman whose father used to wake her as a child to tell her how much he hated her; a woman who was forced to share a bed with her mother as she sobbed her heart out, night after night, at the death of her husband; a man who was physically tortured for hours on end by his sadistic father; a woman who, as a child, used to lay in bed listening to her parents arguing and physically attacking one-another; a woman who was sexually abused by her father; a man who was never allowed to do anything for himself – every time he tried his father would take over and do it 'properly'; another who was never allowed to show 'negative' emotions; another who was never allowed her own thoughts, and many, many others whose childhoods were frightening and confusing, and who have reached adulthood feeling frightened, unlovable, and deeply ashamed and inadequate.

People like this don't always wear their pain like a badge – we tend to cope really well and function really well, too. In fact, I find humans to be incredibly courageous, and it is a great pleasure and joy to see them divesting themselves of all the pain. Jeez – no wonder we love the animals, who show us unconditional love.

I have seen many, many people's lives transformed, within the space of a couple of days (and sometimes minutes), when they have been able to bring out these traumatic memories and remove them from their 'energy bodies'. This statement is based upon the belief that all of our experiences are stored in a sort of energy matrix in and around our bodies, and also upon the fact that I have seen how it is possible to de-energise and release traumatic memories which hitherto have paralysed the individuals so that they cannot deal effectively with stress. These traumatic memories are also, in my opinion, why so many people make fear-based decisions which are unhelpful to the life on this planet.

Background

It seems to me that the way we are running our lives, and the planet, isn't working as well as it could work. Much of this is down to the beliefs we have about the world, and the way we perceive we should fit into it.

We can see the genetic/behavioural link mentioned above fairly clearly in dogs. Although all of my dogs of the same breed have their own unique personalities, the breed itself is known for its bidability and sensitivity. They were bred historically to be gundogs, and their temperaments suit this task. It seems to me that the most sensitive, bonded and attuned of this sensitive breed are the same individuals who suffer from immune-mediated diseases, once again showing the close alignment between the immune system and the emotions.

I believe that it is possible to treat undesirable inherited personality traits, and the consequent effects on the immune system, using energy therapies such as EFT, whose explanation can be found in quantum physics. I also believe that it is possible to treat any negative 'energies' that were picked up from our mothers while we were in the womb. This belief is based upon my own empirical experience, but I do believe that research could verify this experience.

The roots of stress – our early childhood

Much has been done by brave pioneers who, suffering from the effects of their own dysfunctional childhoods, set out to understand the effects in adulthood of childhood trauma experiences, and to offer ways in which the damage can be ameliorated. I cannot recommend strongly enough any of the books by Alice Miller, Pia Mellody or John Bradshaw in this respect. I would also add that, even if you think you had a happy childhood, it is worth reading the following information. You may find it helpful for yourself, and you will certainly find a way to understand and maybe even forgive others.

We develop our sense of self, who we are, from our families. The world presented itself to us as babies through our parents. Babies cannot survive without care; they are essentially helpless. As babies, even before we could understand words, we needed to know that we could count on someone outside of us to be there for us. If we had a parent, or parents, who were predictable, who touched us and approved of us, then we were able to develop a sense that the world was safe, and that we were essentially OK. If we were lucky, we had a parent with whom we could safely form a bond: someone who would show a level of unconditional love, who would know how to meet our needs rather than expect us, subconsciously, to do something that children cannot do, which is to meet their parents' needs.

If we were lucky, we were born into a family where both parents were able to give and receive love, who liked and loved themselves and were consequently able to like and love others. If we were lucky, our parents wouldn't have made unreasonable demands upon us, expecting us to be perfect, or to share their beliefs or think or act exactly like them. Our growing autonomy wouldn't have been threatening to them. If we were lucky, our parents will have taught us where we end and they begin and, consequently, where other people end and begin. Our emotions – our tears, tempers, exuberance and sense of wonder - won't have been threatening to our parents. We will have learnt that it's OK to express how we feel, and they will have taught us balance in this respect.

If we were lucky, our parents will have been able to teach us how to relate to other human beings with tolerance and acceptance. Having taught us that we were essentially OK, we will have learnt that, being human, sometimes we get it right, and sometimes we get it wrong, and that's OK. It's the nature of being human: we are perfectly imperfect. We will have learnt that we are neither better than any other human being, nor worse than any other human being – that none of us is God, and none of us is the devil.

If we were lucky, our parents would have talked to us and listened to us. They won't have yelled at us or beaten us, or made us feel ashamed of who we are. They won't have taught us that we are unlovable and unworthy; neither will they have taught us that we need to be someone or do something in order to gain approval. We won't feel driven to achieve to prove our sense of worth, or to give up trying altogether, having abandoned our sense of worth.

If we were lucky, our parents will have taught us how to care for ourselves. They won't have neglected our developmental needs, expecting us to achieve things that we were incapable of achieving, or doing things for us that we ought to have been taught to do for ourselves. They will have taught us balance and moderation in a world that is essentially safe.

Unfortunately, very few of us are that lucky. Most of us were placed on the planet, having been told that we have to get from A to Z, and no-one gave us an accurate map! Our programming is essentially faulty because our parents' programming was essentially faulty –no-one can teach you something that they themselves do not know.

Consequently, the vast majority of us suffer from existential angst. Very few people like themselves, truly like themselves.

The messages we received from our parents have been further compounded by the society in which we live. The school system teaches us to be ashamed of who we are. If a child becomes a failure at school, this is associated with being a failure as a person. Other children become super-achievers in order to pacify their already existent, parent-taught, sense of worthlessness. As paradoxical as it may seem, the student at the top of the class and the student at the bottom of the class may be equal in their core-felt lack of self-esteem. Whilst the child labelled a failure may have given up on himself, the super-achiever, unable to esteem himself, is often looking for others to endorse his worth as a human being.

As we age, our peer groups mirror ourselves back to us, just as our parents did, except they do this through their own faulty programming. The peer group, however, is often much more unfor-giving than our parents. They lay down all sorts of rules and regulations that we must follow in order to feel validated. We must dress in a certain way, look a certain way. We must fit in with a vast array of codes of conduct that probably, confusingly, don't conform to the codes of conduct we have already been taught in the home. And we must be able to express ourselves, communicate, in an acceptable way.

Believe me, this isn't easy; not everyone is good at communicating, and it's so easy to misunderstand.

Individuality is stifled by the society in which we live. Society, for example, often values left-brained skills such as logic, science and maths, far more than it values right-brained skills such as creativity, intuition and emotions. Further, as society favours left-brain activities, those who possess them in abundance are given permission to act sanctimoniously towards others, thereby making themselves feel better and transferring their inner sense of unworthiness to others.

Some of us have been programmed to know that it's acceptable to cry. Others haven't, and if we cry in their presence, then we become very threatening. Some of us have been taught that it's acceptable to express our thoughts and feelings, even if they go against the thoughts and feelings of another. To some, this is very threatening – their programming does not allow; they have been shamed to the core for expressing themselves in such a way, and see it as shameful if someone else does.

Interestingly, the people we don't like are often the people who are expressing the behaviours and emotions that we, as children, were trained not to have or show. It doesn't make these people bad. Rather, they give us a chance to look within and reclaim the disallowed parts of ourselves.

And so we are taught to repress our thoughts and emotions. We obtain permission to do this in a rigid, structured way by obtaining 'qualifications' that someone else hands down to us. And those with qualifications try to keep those of us without them in line, invalidating another's right to have a view.

John Bradshaw, writing in *Bradshaw on the Family*, says:

'We are taught to be nice and polite. We are taught that these behaviours (most often lies) are better than telling the truth. Our churches, schools and politics are rampant with teaching dishonesty (saying things we don't mean, and pretending to feel ways we don't feel). We smile when we feel sad; laugh nervously when dealing with grief; laugh at jokes we don't think are funny; tell people things to be polite that we surely don't mean.'

Eventually, if we've been really well programmed, we actually lose touch with what we think and feel. We have been taught that the genuine emotions and thoughts we had were wrong, and so we disown them and disassociate from them, and we don't know where or who we

202

are anymore. The world is frightening and painful, and the rules are so confusing that we cannot possibly get it right – even if we appear to be getting it right. Many of us function as shining stars in public, but do our despairing in private.

And so it is that, when life happens as it does to all of us, some of us are better able to cope with it than others. It's about the level of honesty we have been programmed to feel, think, and express – about ourselves, and about the world around us. It is, essentially, about our ability to see things as they *are* as opposed to how we *believe* they are supposed to be. It is our ability to accept what is, and remain comfortable to be us, that determines whether or not we will be able to deal healthily with the stressful situations that life presents to us.

At its core, stress is about how much we love and value ourselves or, conversely, how badly we feel about ourselves. If we cannot love ourselves, cherish ourselves, or trust our own feelings, or feel entitled to just *be* without having to prove ourselves to anyone . . . then life is very stressful indeed.

Our software matrix

I think it is safe to say that every thought and emotion we ever had about ourselves in relation to the world is stored either in our brain or, as I believe, in an energy or 'software matrix' within our bodies. These memories can be triggered by outside stimuli. I have a memory, for example, of lying on the grass on a beautiful summer's day when I was about twelve, and feeling totally and deeply at peace. I just have to see a deep blue sky to travel back to that experience.

Less helpfully, the vast majority of us have memories of being shamed as children, of being made to feel 'less than'. Others have memories, frequently buried in their subconscious, of being expected to fulfil a need in their parents that they, as children, were simply unable to fulfil. Daddy's little Princess, and Mummy's little Prince might understand what I mean.

When these negative memories are triggered, we experience a disruption in our energy bodies. You will be able to recognise this disruption if you've ever had a phobia. You know logically, for example, that the spider, or elevator, or snake is not going to harm you. And yet the very mention of the object of your phobia will have you shuddering, shaking and sweating. It's as though the electric circuit in your body has short-circuited. No logic nor reason will persuade you that you're safe.

Similar energy body disruptions are triggered by people, places, smells, songs, beliefs, and events that touch upon a core belief that we are unlovable, unworthy, or just not good enough. An example might be of a woman who, as a child, was subjected to intense rage from her father. As an adult, when a man who has authority over her expresses anger, that stored memory is triggered and she falls to pieces and cannot deal with him logically.

It is emotionally suicidal for a child to admit that her father, on whom she relies for survival, is faulty in any way. So instead of seeing her father's rage as what it is – her father's rage – she transfers the blame to herself. If it's her fault, then at least she can 'be better'. So it is, for a child, that everything that happens to her is absorbed in a very egocentric way. If you grew up in a family where your parents were not at peace with themselves or those around them, then you take it all upon your shoulders, feeling at your core that you are defective. This emotion, or energy, is therefore stored in your memory, ready to be triggered.

Similarly, if you were taught as a child that you are not allowed to own or express anger, as an example, when anger is triggered as part of the flight or fight mechanism (as anger is a vital component of self-protection), because you have been programmed not to feel it, you will be split. You will feel intense shame at feeling anger. The ability to acknowledge the anger, let alone discharge it, as it has been covered by shame, is not available to you. You become overwhelmed. You cannot cope with your own emotions in any rational or constructive way. The emotion is therefore either repressed, which can lead to stress-related illness, or it is projected onto someone else, or discharged in an immoderate way, which can lead to equally unwanted consequences and further stress.

This is the energy body disruption I speak of, and it applies to all of the emotions you have been programmed not to feel; and all of the triggers which remind you, often at a subconscious level, that you are defective, unworthy, and powerless.

Most people – unless they were raised consciously (and few of us have been, since our parents cannot teach us something they themselves have not been taught) – have deep internal programming that runs a negative script about themselves. These include beliefs like:

I don't like myself
I'm a failure
Nobody would like me if they really knew me
I'm lazy
I'm ugly
I'm a moaner
I'm not good enough
I'm selfish
I'm mediocre
I'm not worth paying
I'm not worthy of love
I'm over-confident
I want to die
Life is too hard for me
I need to do better
I am better than others
My qualifications/marital status/job validate me as a human being
etc., etc., etc.

Now, you may be sitting here thinking that you don't ever have these or other negative thoughts about yourself, but I would submit that if anyone outside of yourself has the power to make you feel overwhelmingly angry or deeply shamed, or if unwanted events such as redundancy and financial troubles keep you awake at night and bring up feelings of intense shame, then they are triggering the energy body disturbance that comes when your software matrix which stores such thoughts is activated.

As an example, if someone told me that they thought I was cold-hearted, they wouldn't upset me in the least, because I know that I am not. I would, though – before I worked on myself – have had a huge energy body disruption if someone tried to force me to do or think something I didn't feel comfortable doing or thinking. When I was a child, obedience in children was valued and demanded; my thoughts and feelings were frequently invalidated (which explains a lot about me, and why I run CHC, and also illustrates that God can use our faults!).

I believe that our ability to handle stress can be improved if we work on the negative beliefs we have about ourselves, and that we will also find ourselves in less conflict with the world as a result. This means first going within to find out what they are (since we often don't know we have these negative thoughts about ourselves). Then we dump them.

We can do this by journaling – writing about them so that we can understand what is going on inside our heads and letting unhelpful beliefs go; and we can do it by reading books that will reframe our beliefs about ourselves (some of which are in the recommended reading list at the back of this book). We can also attend counselling; or we can use energy therapies such as Emotional Freedom Technique, Thought Field Therapy, and BodyTalk to literally wipe this faulty programming from our metaphorical hard discs. Transactional Analysis and Neurolinguistic Programming can also help. The Flower Remedies are also brilliant at helping us to resolve emotional issues.

However we do it, I can guarantee that it will lead you to a place where you are emotionally and physically healthier, and your animals will reflect your health.

Radical reprogramming for stress resolution

I have a magnet on my fridge which says, 'Dear Lord, please help me be the person my dog thinks I am'. It's funny how the dogs see the good in us. Maybe, just maybe, they are right to have faith in us? Perhaps we should start to look at ourselves from our dogs' eyes, and perhaps this will see an end to the stress we feel.

To be free of stress, to be free of illness, to move to the next stage of human evolution, we need to reprogramme the way we think, so that we are able to look at reality, and not at what other people tell us ought to be. The first stage of this process is that all the 'stuff', all the untrue beliefs we've been burying, must rise to the surface: all the stuff we've been holding onto that we don't want to look at.

We have been given, at this time in human evolution, a number of powerful techniques to help us remove the energy body disruption that arises when negative memories, and false beliefs about ourselves, are triggered.

Daniel Benor MD is a psychiatrist in New Jersey who became unhappy with the way in which his profession had moved away from psychotherapy and towards drugs. He says, 'I was led to discover a series of self-healing approaches that readily lend themselves to brief therapist interventions. Eye Movement Desensitisation and Reprocessing (EMDR) was a blessing to me and my clients. Negative feelings and beliefs, even intense ones, are rapidly relieved and transformed to positive ones with this method.

'I then learned to use Emotional Freedom Technique (EFT). In EFT you tap or press a finger at a series of acupuncture points on your face, chest and hand, while reciting an affirmation. Because it works more rapidly than EMDR and does not evoke intense emotional releases, it can be used as self-healing.'

In addition to finding and reprogramming negative thoughts we have about ourselves, I also believe we need to understand a few 'Tribal' or systemic proclivities that do not help us as individuals, or society as a whole. The first disadvantage many of us face is that we haven't been taught about boundaries. I find it an interesting concept, incidentally, that as our emotions and our immune systems mirror one-another, we may well strengthen our immune defences if we first strengthen our emotional defences. As animals mirror their owners (a word I don't like to use in relation to animals, but there you go), then if we strengthen our boundaries, then theirs will be strengthened too.

Boundaries

According to Pia Mellody, boundaries are defined as invisible and symbolic 'fences' that have three purposes: 1) to keep people from coming into our space and abusing us, 2) to keep us from going into the space of others and abusing them, and 3) to give each of us a way to embody our sense of who we are. I discussed external and internal boundaries in chapter 7.

Boundaries are taught, but in dysfunctional families where parents themselves have faulty boundaries, this cannot happen. This leads to four types of damaged boundary systems which, themselves, are responsible for a huge amount of stress. (If our boundaries were healthy, the outside world and circumstances would have far less power to hurt us.)

People with *nonexistent boundaries* have no sense of being abused or of being abusive; they are incredibly vulnerable and can paradoxically sometimes be injurious to be around.

People with *damaged boundaries* can at certain times or with certain individuals say no, set limits and take care of themselves. At other times, or with other people, they are powerless to set boundaries. People with damaged boundaries only have partial awareness of other people's boundaries, and so in certain circumstances they step into someone else's life and try to control or manipulate them.

A *system of walls* substitutes for a healthy boundary, and is often made up of either anger or fear. People who use a wall of anger give off the message (either verbally or non verbally) 'if you come near me or say anything about such and such, I'll explode'. A wall of noise is another 'racket' used: if I keep talking I won't have to hear anything that's threatening. Another type of wall is a wall of silence. The wall of fear keeps people isolated.

The fourth type of boundary impairment lies in *moving from a wall to nonexistent boundaries and back again*. Experiencing life when you have no boundaries is painful, so a person in this instance will risk it occasionally, and then retreat behind the wall.

As I said earlier, when you can name something it ceases to have power over you. Start by observing where your boundary system fails you. Be aware that you are allowed to say 'no', and that it is not only OK for you to have your own thoughts, feelings and behaviours, but that it is absolutely essential. Also be aware when you find yourself trying to tell others how to think, feel and act. You may believe that you are being helpful when you do this but, in reality, you are attempting the impossible. We can only control ourselves, and usually only very badly, and it can amount to spiritual abuse when we invalidate another's right to have their reality.

Don't rescue

This is an interesting one, and I have to admit to being a 'recovering rescuer'. Rescuing essentially means doing things for people that they are able to do for themselves. It is probably meant kindly, but it is essentially disempowering. Also, when you've been involved in rescuing people – fixing their problems – they'll put you into the 'rescuer box' and they'll disappear when *you* need help! By all means help others, but don't kill yourself in the process, and don't allow others to dump all their problems on you. They will not thank you in the end.

Allow your emotions

Tribe has told us for so many centuries that emotions are bad. We are trained as children to be 'good', which usually means being quiet and not having any needs or wants. People who explode with rage and anger, for example, are often doing so because they've been told they must not show anger. Instead, they keep it locked inside until, like a pressure cooker, they explode. In some instances they do so because they were subjected to physical and verbal abuse as children, and are carrying their caregiver's rage. This can be discharged using EFT.

When you feel the energy body disruption that is known as anger, it means that you are feeling threatened in some way. Acknowledge it, accept it, and own it if it originated with you. If necessary, throw a cushion or chop some wood to discharge the energy safely. Voice your concerns before that feeling explodes into rage. The person you are voicing your concerns to might not like it, but you have a right to protect yourself and your loved-ones. If the other person doesn't respect your right to do so, then bless them and walk away.

All emotions have a function. Studies have shown, for example, that grief needs to be honoured before a person can heal from it. It's no good stuffing your grief under the carpet. You actually need to allow yourself to feel it fully. Many of us have been trained not to cry – and yet crying is just about the most healing thing you can do. Brandon Bays locked herself into her home for two weeks, warned friends that she wouldn't be contactable, took the phone off the hook, and allowed herself to experience her emotions fully. In doing this, she healed herself of cancer and now hosts workshops for others, showing them how to do the same.

The metaphysical maxim is that you can get beyond any disease you choose to get beyond, but if you stuff your emotions, they stay inside.

The next stage is to start loving yourself, and to start loving your emotions – they were given to us for a purpose. They are messengers, telling us how we are, and we need to listen to them.

The self-empowerment of looking inside

Religions, educational systems, politics, science – every system in society – has a sort of inbuilt mechanism that tells us that if we only follow their advice, if we only discount our own thoughts and feelings, and go with They Who Know Better, then everything will be alright. We are going to have to get over this fallacy. We all remember situations when we did what someone else told us to do, ignoring our own warning signals, and lived to regret it. And we all know of situations where what they thought to be right turned out to be wrong.

If you let go of the limiting untruths you believe about yourself in relation to others, then all of the abilities that you have inside you, all the things you wanted to do but stopped yourself doing, will come out. By getting rid of the beliefs about who we are not, we'll be able to embrace who we are, and trust ourselves more.

This is because, being unafraid to look at ourselves honestly, knowing that we are perfectly imperfect like everyone else, we're not going to be afraid of expressing ourselves, or doing what we believe is the right thing to do. Neither will we need to prevent others from expressing themselves or doing what they need to do. As Pia Mellody says, we'll be able to look at other people's beliefs and opinions, and say, 'oh isn't that interesting'. They won't be able to threaten who you are, because you already know who you are, and you're comfortable with yourself.

If we want to minimise stress, then we're going to have to stop judging ourselves unmercifully! We are all, in fact, unique. We're not meant to be the same as everyone else. You are meant to be you and you know you've always done your best.

Banish fear

We have cloaked ourselves all our lives through fear. This is only logical – it's not easy to be human. Now is the time to gather all the belief you have in yourself, all the trust you have in yourself, and use it to heal *yourself*. This is hard.

Most of us do a great job of helping other people, and many of us take this to the extreme so we aren't even on the List of People Who Matter, let alone at the top of it. Those of us who have animals – and I've been watching myself as well as everyone else – will go to the ends of the earth to help the animals and our fellow humans, but we won't take our vitamins, or eat properly, or take the rest we need, or walk away from discordant or controlling people.

We probably do this because we've been told at some time that we were selfish, or that it's wrong to think of ourselves. But if we realised that our discordant energies (stresses) are affecting everyone around us, maybe we would take another look at that?

Most of us do a great job of helping everyone else but ourselves; we do a great job of helping and healing and working with other people and the animals – but what if we are the one who needs some assistance now? If we start from here, where we are, then maybe we will have more strength with which to help others.

Stress busting in the present

There are a number of techniques that are invaluable when it comes to stress busting. All of them take us out of the worrying, beating-ourselves-up type thoughts that circle in our heads. Walking in nature is one of them, but it is necessary to be conscious of the circling thoughts and to let them go. Instead of being in our heads, the technique is to be conscious of the surroundings, the air on our faces, our feet on the ground, sounds, and so on.

Another technique is to 'pause' periodically throughout the day. Again, it means disconnecting from the madness, the scripts we run inside our heads, and being aware of the present. Feel your feet on the ground, the clothes on your body, the muscles in your body, the air on your face. Just relax, and be.

When you're peeling potatoes, just peel potatoes. Rest your attention in the gap between the knife and the spud. When you're driving, just drive. Rest your attention on the road ahead.

When someone is speaking to you, just listen. Consciously drop the thoughts you have in your head, all the things you're planning to say in response. Just listen. It's amazing what you'll hear.

Forget what needs to be done this afternoon. Just be here now. You'll find if you try this, that you are extremely, overwhelmingly, safe. You'll find that 98% of what we fear just doesn't happen. If you live here, now, in the present, stress and fear have no hold on you.

Inner knowing

Those who have already started on this path will attest that when your energy body is clear of the past, of old pains and untruths, and when your head is free of all the circling thoughts, you are so much more receptive to the truth. The faculties that Tribe has told us we must not use – our inner knowing, our intuition – will come back.

Your sensitivity will rise, and so will your empathic abilities. You'll be able to read people's feelings and emotions. It's important, though, to read the emotions, bless them, and then let them go. Be aware that not all the emotions you feel are your own; you could have absorbed them from people in the supermarket, or you might be carrying the unresolved emotions of your parents from the past. If you are not aware, you will think that every mood you go through is your's. If you're depressed or frightened or angry but don't know why, the chances are that you are carrying someone else's emotion (just like the animals do). If you can't find a root for it, let it go. Use the techniques that are available, and let it all go.

You will also known things before many others do. You will trust yourself, and if you trust yourself, you will love yourself and the life within you. You will love yourself unconditionally and move to the next level. We human beings are moving to the point where we are so in love with life, so in love with each other, that we will stop holding ourselves back. Too many people tell us that if we cross their palms with silver we will be healthy, wealthy, spiritual or wise. We're going to do it anyway – with or without their help. It's our birthright!

A book is just an opinion, a newspaper is just a slant on a story – it's not absolute. Believe and trust in yourself. You know as much as anyone else.

Recognise who you are – not who someone gives you permission to be. Nobody has the right to hold judgment against you, and tell you that you're not good enough. You *are* good enough! Dump the guilt and blame. And if someone doesn't treat you the way you need to be treated, bless them and walk away.

Being at peace

My journey has taught me that if we want peace on this planet, we must make peace within ourselves. The same applies to love: if we want love, we need to be loving. The misperception here is that in order to be loving, we have to please everyone else. No. When we try to please everyone else, they just move the goalposts.

To be loving, we have to first love ourselves, and by this I mean that we have to accept ourselves and stop beating ourselves up. I can honestly say that I've never done anything except my best, even though I've made mistakes. And if I believe this about myself, then I have to believe it about everyone else. We all do our best, based upon the knowledge and experience we have at the time. And if we don't impose unnecessary limitations upon ourselves, then our knowledge and experience can only expand. We also need to keep on discarding what doesn't fit us, what doesn't work for us, and accept that we have a right and a duty to speak the truth.

Living life

A kindly being once said to me, 'Live life to the utmost of your ability – really experiencing life, playing with it, loving it. Live life now. Love your bodies, love the environment, love the animals, love your creator. There is nothing to fear. Live life beyond your wildest expectations. Live life as if you are a spiritual being having a human experience. Celebrate your life. Love your life. Love yourself.'

If you love your life, if you choose to stay on the planet, illness will have no hold on you. I'm not saying this is easy to achieve – but I am saying it is possible. The animals, who are also spiritual beings having a physical experience, can see the truth of who you are. Follow their lead, and go for the gold within your heart.

What choices should you make?

I am very conscious that this book does not give anyone any prescriptive courses of action to follow. Some readers will therefore be left not knowing what to do for the best where their animals are concerned. This is deliberate, because I don't know everything. Neither does anyone else, for that matter. We're kidding ourselves if we believe someone else can prevent us from having to 'skirt the abyss and feel the void under our feet'. Others can help, provide information, point us in the right direction – but I hope that I have illustrated that, as our animals have shown us, the process is about becoming More for ourselves.

If you haven't yet made up your mind about whether to give puppy shots and the first year's booster; whether to vaccinate annually; whether to vaccinate every three years; or whether to use nosodes . . . and if you're left wondering which food is the right food for your dog, cat or horse, then the chances are you're having difficulty making a decision based upon so many different viewpoints. I know how you feel!

This means that it's down to you. There is no-one to tell you what to do. When you have your beloved animal's wellbeing at stake, however, it's not necessarily comfortable to be in this position.

Every one of us has an inbuilt intuition, or an inner knowing, and this is a good time to try it out. Once you learn how to do this, then life will become significantly more joyful for you, and far less stressful. You are also less likely to make mistakes based upon someone else's faulty belief system. By all means listen to all the views – but make your own choices.

If you have to ask whether you should do something, then something inside you is stopping you. You need to ask yourself three questions in relation to the subject you are making a decision about:

1.   Is it true?
2.   Is it untrue?
3.   Do I need more information from which to make a decision?

If you aren't sure, then more study could be required. If you're still not sure, then perhaps you need to get in touch with your own inner knowing.

Imagine you are just about to vaccinate your pet, or that you're going to feed your dog raw food (in short, imagine yourself in the position you need to make a choice about). Go inside yourself, and ask yourself how you feel knowing that you are going to do it. Do you feel good, or do you feel awful?

Now ask yourself where you feel that good or bad feeling. If you feel it in your head or your stomach, ask yourself the question again, but feel the answer in your heart. If your heart leaps with joy, then do it. If it doesn't, then don't do it.

Everything you need is inside of you, waiting to unfold. Your intuition will also lead you to the sources of information that will help expand your view. Use your inner knowing to sift through the maze.

This, my dear friends, is the ultimate shock to the system that needs to happen now: we are building a planet upon which every human, every animal, is self-determined, knowledgeable, confident, and coming from a place of peace and love. Shocking, perhaps, but without the brave people who demonstrated the efficacy of this approach, we would have no cars, no hot showers, no television, no telephone, no educational system, no printing presses, no racial equality, no rights for women . . .

We need people who will step out from the illusion, the received wisdom, and try it another way. We need to hold each others' hands as we walk to the cliff edge to discover that we can fly.

This is what the animals came to teach us; they would like nothing better than for us to transmute their pain into gold.

Recommended Reading

Natural Nutrition for Dogs and Cats by Kymythy R. Schultze
Raw Meaty Bones by Tom Lonsdale
The Nature of Animal Healing by Martin Goldstein
Give Your Dog a Bone by Ian Billinghurst
The Holistic Guide for a Healthy Dog by Wendy Volhard &
Kerry Brown
The Complete Herbal Book for the Dog by Juliette de Bairacli
Levy
Natural Dog Care by Celeste Yarnall,
The Encyclopedia of Natural Pet Care by C.J. Puotinen
Reigning Cats and Dogs by Pat McKay
The Natural Way for Dogs and Cats by Midi Fairgrieve
Thorsons Complete Guide to Vitamins and Minerals by Leornard
Mervyn
Facing Codependence by Pia Mellody
Bradshaw on the Family by John Bradshaw
Thou Shalt not be Aware by Alice Miller
The Power of Now by Eckhart Tolle

Web Sites

Raw Meaty Bones http://www.rawmeatybones.com/
Natural Diet http://www.volhard.com/holistic/artbywv.htm
Raw Diet with raw bones
http://www.alternativepethealth.com/canine-diet.html
The Senior Dogs Project http://siriusdog.com
Canine Health Concern www.canine-health-concern.org.uk
www.critterfixer.com education of pet owners
www.vaccinationnews.com vaccinations and adverse reactions
www.ukrmb.co.uk/ support and action group
www.ivis.org/advances/Infect_Dis_Carmichael/schultz/chapter_f
rm.asp?LA=1 R.D. Schultz Vaccination Information
www.shorti-online.org vaccine associated sarcomas in cats

References to some further studies not carried in the main text of this book

Scientific papers on vaccine reactions in horses can be found at the National Library of Medicine web sit - http://www.ncbi.nlm.nih.gov/, *including:*

Adverse reactions to equine vaccinations: a preliminary survey.
Vet Rec. 1988 Apr 16;122(16):396.
Possible basis of adverse reactions to vaccination against equine influenza.
Vet Rec. 1993 Jun 26;132(26):658-9
Reactions to equine 'flu vaccination.
Vet Rec. 1988 Apr 16;122(16):373
Effects of equine influenza and tetanus vaccination on pulmonary function in normal and chronic obstructive pulmonary disease affected horses.
Equine Vet J. 1996 Mar;28(2):157-60.
Reactions to influenza vaccination.
Vet Rec. 1986 Mar 1;118(9):251-2.
Reactions to equine influenza vaccination.
Vet Rec. 1986 Apr 12;118(15):435. No abstract available. Erratum in: Vet Rec 1986 Apr 19;118(16):468.
Bilateral optic neuropathy associated with influenza vaccination.
J Neuroophthalmol. 1996 Sep;16(3):182-4.
Field study of physicians on the incidence of adverse vaccine effects and vaccine reactions in early summer meningoencephalitis, tetanus and influenza vaccination in general practice]
Wien Med Wochenschr. 1998;148(8-9):214-5. German
Reactions to influenza vaccination.
Vet Rec. 1986 Mar 29;118(13):371
Reactions to equine influenza vaccination.
Vet Rec. 1988 Oct 1;123(14):379.